PENGUIN BOOKS
THE PENGUIN NEW WRITING IN SRI LANKA

D.C.R.A. Goonetilleke was born in 1938 in Colombo and grew up in the suburb of Nugegoda where he still lives. He studied at Royal College, Colombo, and read English at the University of Ceylon. Choosing to embark on an academic career, he obtained a Ph.D. at the University of Lancaster, U.K., and is now Professer and Head of the Department of English, University of Kelaniya, Sri Lanka. He has been a Visiting Scholar in the Faculty of English at the University of Cambridge as well as a Fellow Commoner of Churchill College. He has also held the Foundation Visiting Fellowship of Clare Hall, Cambridge, and has been awarded a Henry Charles Chapman Visiting Fellowship by the Institute of Commonwealth Studies, University of London. His books include three published by Macmillan (London): *Developing Countries in British Fiction* (1977), *Images of the Raj*: *South Asia in the Literature of the Empire* (1988) and *Joseph Conrad*: *Beyond Culture and Background* (1990). He has also edited three anthologies, *Modern Sri Lankan Stories*, *Modern Sri Lankan Poetry* and *Modern Sri Lankan Drama*; written a book of essays, *Between Cultures*: *Essays on Literature, Language and Education*; and published numerous articles in international journals.

Professor Goonetilleke is married and has two sons.

D1211373

The Penguin
New Writing
in Sri Lanka

Edited with an Introduction by

D.C.R.A. Goonetilleke

PENGUIN BOOKS

Penguin Books India (P) Ltd., B4/246, Safdarjung Enclave, New Delhi 110 029, India
Penguin Books Ltd., Harmondsworth, Middlesex, England
Penguin Books USA Inc., 375 Hudson Street, New York 10014, U.S.A.
Penguin Books Australia Ltd., Ringwood, Victoria, Australia
Penguin Books Canada Ltd., 10, Alcorn Avenue, Suite 300, Toronto, Ontario M4V 382, Canada
Penguin Books (N.Z.) Ltd., 182-190 Wairau Road, Auckland 10, New Zealand

This selection first published by Penguin Books India (P) Ltd., 1992

Copyright © D.C.R.A. Goonetilleke 1991, 1992

Typeset in New Baskerville by Transcriptions, Delhi
Made and printed by Ananda Offset Private Ltd., Calcutta

To my dear sons—

Surendra and Dilhan

Acknowledgements

The editor and publisher would like to thank the writers and translators whose works appear in this anthology.

The following sources are also gratefully acknowledged: Godfrey Gunatillake's 'The Garden' from *Sankha I* (1958), ed. Donald Abeysinghe; Punyakante Wijenaike's 'The Third Woman' from *The Third Woman* (Colombo, 1963); Suvimalee Karunaratne's 'The Golden Oriole' from *Bili Pooja* (Colombo, Hansa, 1973); James Goonewardene's 'The Doughty Men of Purantota' from *The Awakening of Doctor Kirthi* (Colombo: Lake House Investments, 1976); Ranjini Obeyesekere's 'Despair' from *Hemisphere*; J. S. Tissainayagam's 'Misunderstanding' from *Kaduwa I* (1983), ed. Quadri Ismail; Patrick Fernando's poems from *The Return of Ulysses* (London, Hand & Flower Press, 1955); translations from *An Anthology of Modern Writing from Sri Lanka*, ed. Ranjini Obeyesekere and Chitra Fernando (University of Arizona Press, 1981); *Journal of South Asian Literature*, Vol.22, No. 1, 1987, guest-ed. Ranjini Obeyesekere; *An Anthology of Sinhalese Literature of the Twentieth Century*, ed. C.H.B. Reynolds (Kent, Paul Norbury, 1987).

Contents

Part III: Writing in Tamil

Introduction

This is the first attempt to edit an anthology of Sri Lankan literature in all its three languages, Sinhalese, Tamil and English. Our literature has suffered a cruel fate. Outsiders have generally turned a blind eye to it, regarding it a mere extension of the literature of India or as being of no consequence; they unconsciously equate literary quality with the island's physical diminutiveness and political and economic insignificance. Insiders have undervalued it and, in the case of the literature in English, have even periodically prophesied its demise. But the survival of the literature of Sri Lanka—the literature in each language is distinctive, yet recognizably the product of the same country—is no exception to the general rule: it depends fortunately and primarily on the creative writers. They have not merely continued to write but, after having been inhibited, even suffocated, for four-hundred-and-fifty years under the colonial domination of the Portuguese, the Dutch and, finally, the British, they have, after Independence (1948), rapidly brought about an efflorescence. The present anthology seeks to capture this achievement which, I venture to say, compares favourably in quality with good literature written in English, and in other languages too, elsewhere.

*

Sri Lanka was granted independence by Britain mainly as a consequence of the freedom struggle in India. Because its independence was won more easily—in fact, too easily—the Sri Lankans did not forge as strong a national consciousness as the Indians. Indeed, neither country has been fully successful in this regard, if we are to judge by the separatist tendencies in both countries at the present time, but Sri Lanka has been much the less successful of the two, especially given the comparative smallness of scale of its problems, though these are no less acute than India's. Frantz Fanon argues that violence is necessary in the process of decolonization as it unifies and truly liberates the native people[1], but I do not wish to endorse this stand, mindful of the fact that violence can be in itself an evil. It has its costs in human and other terms. Even after Independence, the ruling and social elites in Sri Lanka consisted of 'brown sahibs'. Yet, before long, in 1956, nationalist currents did surface, however extremist they might have been, and 1956 is, in several ways, a watershed in contemporary Sri Lankan history. Elected Prime Minister in that year, the late Mr S.W.R.D. Bandaranaike was the architect of changes of which he himself lost control. The adoption of a national dress instead of the top hat and coat-tails was more than a symbolic change. English was displaced from its pre-eminent position as the official language and the medium of instruction in schools and universities. English had to be relegated to the status of a second language, sooner or later, despite the regrets of the English-educated classes, but it was not properly treated as a second language. It was neglected for two decades and even reviled. Paradoxically, it was in this context that literature in English by Sri Lankans came into prominence (of course, it did exist before 1956). Faced with the loss of, or at least a significant diminution of, their privileges, the English-educated became more aware of themselves and the social, cultural and literary context in which they lived. Their response to the changes of 1956 was negative rather than positive, yet paradoxically it led to fruitful results in the field of creative writing.

This historical explanation is not the complete story. The influence of the critical work and the standards of the Department of English in our single University in the 1930s and 40s spread beyond the portals of the University. The University Dramatic Society, under the guidance of the then Professor of English, E.F.C. Ludowyk, was the leading theatre group in the country and set the standards in the production and choice of plays. At that time, young graduates founded journals such as *Harvest, Symposium, Community* and *Points of View*, which gave expression to their critical and creative preoccupations and maintained credible standards. Their counterparts in the media dealt with literary matters on the same high level. All this created a climate for writing and the beginnings of a literary tradition. Of course, the imaginative writing itself, as it later turned out, came from those who had been to university (such as Patrick Fernando, Yasmine Gooneratne and Chitra Fernando) as well as from those who had not (such as Punyakante Wijenaike, Lakdasa Wikkramasinha and Basil Fernando).

Literature in English did not appear as a consequence of a willed movement. It came into being and did not draw attention to itself and was not recognized, until recently, late in the day. The Sri Lankan novel in English has now come of age, but the writers of fiction have excelled as authors of short stories for quite some time. The short story in English has established itself in modern times as a genre important in itself.

*

Stories like Punyakante Wijenaike's 'The Third Woman' and James Goonewardene's 'The Doughty Man of Purantota' deal with the rural experience, while all the writers are urban and English-educated, whatever their early connections with the village. Characteristically, the writers in English are conscious of being alienated from the masses and local traditions by virtue of their English affiliations. Contemplating the countryside or rural characters is, in a way, an attempt to capture a truly national, authentically Sri Lankan, experience, and find roots in the soil. When successful, the writers are able to overcome the barriers that separate them from their subject and, by means of their imagination, enter into rural experience and milieux; they avoid the common tendency to romanticize the village.

Punyakante Wijenaike does not appear to be deeply versed in literature or literary criticism, but she is a natural and original writer. In 'The Third Woman', she gets inside the skin of the peasants and powerfully suggests a theme—unmotivated evil—whose import is not limited to the peasantry. The loose domestic relations depicted in the story, have an actual social basis in the 'upcountry' areas of Sri Lanka. What the narrator regards as his everlasting love for his mistress is shown up by the writer's irony (operating beyond the narrator's consciousness) as infatuation. The story is sombre, but it is not cynical or despairing. It is informed by Wijenaike's compassion, her main strength as a writer.

James Goonewardene has been criticized for projecting 'romantic village idylls' in his novels, *A Quiet Place* (1968) and *Call of the Kirala* (1971),[2] but his collection of stories, *The Awakening of Doctor Kirthi* (1976), from which I have taken 'The

Doughty Men of Purantota', is marked by disillusionment. The story focuses mainly on Girigoris, an impotent hunchback whose wife has eloped with a toddy tapper from a neighbouring village and who is chief lay custodian of the temple at the time of the action. He has 'waited in silence all these years nursing his numerous grievances, building up his hate, waiting for the time when he would become master of the village'. The time comes when a bridge is to be built on the doorstep of the village. The story becomes so intense as to intimate allegorical suggestions: on the social and political plane, of how men rise to become ruthless dictators and others become their mindless slaves and, on the moral plane, of how evil is embedded in the nature of things.

Our writers in English began to contemplate the world to which they belong and the world they know best—the urban world of the English-educated and English-speaking classes—as early as they began contemplating the rural milieu. Godfrey Gunatillake, in 'The Garden' (1958), captures the middle-class world beautifully. The story focuses on the marital relationship between Tissa and Prema, in which a surface contentment, even complacency, masks the separateness of the partners deep down. The writer's prose is delicate, precise and often poetic. The poetry resides not only in continuous local touches but, more importantly, in the overall symbolism of the Garden of Eden. The serpent, metaphorically and literally, enters Tissa's 'paradise'.

The writers, however, did concentrate on rural experience in the early decades and it was only in the 1970s that, while not turning their backs on the village, they began to focus their attention more often on their own world. In 'The Golden Oriole', Suvimalee Karunaratne, with an irony that is humorous, sympathetic and acute, depicts the burgeoning of love in a spinster, stimulating her to step out of her wonted character as a staid and religious teacher, putting off her suitor because she gets romantic, and failing while still confident of the outcome. The golden oriole and the two brown mynahs (at the end of the story) impart an illuminating flash of symbolism to the realistic fabric.

Chitra Fernando, in 'The Perfection of Giving', is preoccupied with the more Oriental, Sinhalese, provincial middle class and exposes the mixture of spiritualism and materialism found in this society. There are signs, in the story, that this kind of society is changing, though very slowly. The perfection of giving is one of the ten perfections which one aspiring to be the Buddha cultivates. The writer is critical not only of society, how it distorts Buddhist values in practice, but also of the values themselves, though in a muted way. She finally goes beyond an examination of Buddhist values to raise a larger question regarding the dispensation of justice in life, though she does not proceed to an Absurdist extreme of portraying human existence as planless and meaningless.

J.S. Tissainayagam's story 'Misunderstanding' was written when he was an undergraduate; he has been a sharp observer of the social scene from then on and has the kind of detachment necessary for mature writing. He opens up a different milieu, the University, which was touched on in 'The Perfection of Giving', and brings us to the immediate present, dramatizing a problem that has proved disruptive—the gulf between the English-educated and the vernacular-educated, a result of post-1956 language policies in education.

The stories include the work of three generations of writers and three decades of writing. They bring out diverse facets of Sri Lanka's contemporary experience and the changes undergone by its society.

The visions of the writers lend to them a relevance and significance beyond the shores of Sri Lanka. The achievement of our poets in English is of the same kind, though the poetry is generally less 'social' in content than the fiction, but we are on surer grounds in making claims.

When our poets began to feel nationalist currents keenly after 1956, whatever the reactions to them, their central problem was that which faced all poets in ex-colonies at the same stage of literary development—of reconciling their own sensibilities, indigenous traditions and realities on the one hand, and Western literary and other traditions and influences on the other. The problem can be extremely difficult and has led to cultural dislocation in the case of a few writers. However, it ceased to be central or important a decade or two after independence from colonial rule. With 'the clash of cultures' phase now over and behind them, the poets in Sri Lanka and other regions of the Commonwealth write as do their counterparts in Britain or America—out of their personal situations.

The choice or adoption of the English language is usually

regarded as a major problem for the Commonwealth writer. In the words of David Carroll (referring to African writers), 'We are faced with the paradox of a people describing and identifying themselves by means of a foreign language which embodies the values and categories from which they are seeking to free themselves.'[3] In Sri Lanka, the English language was taken for granted by many writers and posed no problem to many even during the early stages of our literary development, whereas, in others, it excited strong feelings and even contributed to dislocating personality. In 1965, Lakdasa Wikkramasinha wrote:

> 'I have come to realize that I am using the language of the most despicable and loathsome people on earth; I have no wish to extend its life and range, enrich its totality.
>
>   To write in English is a form of cultural treason. I have had for the future to think of a way of circumventing this treason; I propose to do this by making my writing entirely immoralist and destructive.'[4]

On the other hand, Yasmine Gooneratne takes to the English language without trauma and even approaches it as a lover in her poem, 'This Language, This Woman'.

The diverse responses of creative writers to English and their tendency to make the language of literature an issue especially during the early stages (that is, soon after Independence) of Commonwealth literature are valid, but not the arbitrary and simplistic demands of critics. It is the generally accepted view of twentieth-century poets and critics that the language of poetry is most effective, if not, only effective, when it reflects the idiom of everyday speech. T.S. Eliot argued: '. . . poetry has primarily to do with the expression of feeling and emotion. . . . Emotion and feeling are best expressed in the common language of the people—that is, in the language common to all classes: the structure, the rhythm, the sound, the idiom of a language, express the personality of the people which speaks it. . . a poet must take as his material his own language as it is actually spoken around him.'[5] W.B. Yeats thought: 'In literature, partly from the lack of that spoken word which knits us to normal man, we have lost in personality, in our delight in the whole man—blood, imagination, intellect running together,'[6] and he sets out to make good this supposed loss in his own later poetry. F.R. Leavis, perhaps the most influential critic of this century and the counterpart of Johnson, Coleridge and Matthew Arnold in their day, consistently lauds poets who employ the 'utterance, movement and intonation . . . of the talking voice'[7] (Donne, Hopkins, T.S. Eliot, for instance).

It seems to me, however, that this point of view is vulnerable. It ignores key questions, though it is true that modern poets made a contribution to literature by re-introducing conversational tones after these had been virtually banished for a long time in Romantic rhetoric and musicality (during the Victorian period). Modern linguistics have sharpened our awareness of the varieties of speech and dialects, of regional, class, group and individual variations in the speech of the same language within single countries. From which kind of speech should the language of poetry draw sustenance? Can there be universally applicable touchstones? To what extent does it account for the achievements of modern poetry itself? Despite Yeats' declared view and though F.R. Leavis praised Yeats' later poetry for using 'the idiom and movement of modern speech',[8] the language of Yeats' great poems such as 'Sailing to Byzantium' and 'Among School Children', though incorporating elements of polite educated speech, is basically and in an overall way, stylized. Really, what matters is whether poetry works as poetry, whatever kind of language is employed.

Sri Lankan critics have adapted the position in the West in regard to the language of poetry. It is argued that the language of the Sri Lankan writer should reflect 'in an ideal form the actual rhythms and idiom of living Ceylon English speech'[9] and even further that the language of the Sri Lankan writer in English gains in vitality if 'derived from Sinhala'.[10] My criticism of Western writers and critics applies to their Sri Lankan counterparts. Moreover, to be so conscious of language and pay it special attention is to separate language from content and experience, whereas, in the case of a truly creative writer, his experience will find the language that comes naturally to it; this will determine its components, whether Sri Lankan or British or whatever mix. Lakdasa Wikkramasinha is often eulogized for employing Sri Lankan English in his poetry, yet his use of language is not a simple matter of doing so but is original, incorporating expressions derived from a variety of sources. Moreover, as Wole Soyinka said, 'We are now beyond the "Prospero-Caliban" syndrome of the complexities—which attend the adoption of a language of colonial imposition . . . the "Prospero-Caliban" syndrome is dead.'[11]

In point of actual poetic achievement, Yasmine Gooneratne and Patrick Fernando are Sri Lanka's most talented poets in English. Gooneratne possesses a mastery of the English language and literary forms in her poetry with no problems being caused by their alien-ness, and perhaps her greatest gift is her ability to think in images, especially when she transcends the Westernized upper class to which she belongs. In 'Peace-Game', she does so, and satirically and allegorically contemplates class conflict; the pressure of the poetry is such that it suggests another dimension—international power politics—too. She migrated to Australia in the early '70s. 'Migrant Poet' is taken from her last collection in which she contemplates her experiences from this position and exploits poetic resources other than the wit characteristic of her earlier poetry.

Fernando's first book of poems was published in 1955; the momentous changes of 1956 were not important in his case. Irony is crucial to his work; it is a feature of his technique as well as what shapes his vision of life. It enables him to see contradiction as inherent in, and central to, life, and to reconcile himself to it. See how 'Folly and Wisdom' begins and ends. Fernando's language is polished, minted, yet familiar, conversational, and his forms well-crafted and orthodox. He excels as a satirist. It may appear as if the satire inhibits feeling, but the case is more complex, as 'The Late Sir Henry' reveals; Fernando, concerned about genuine feeling, criticises the lack of it.

Lakdasa Wikkramasinha is different from Gooneratne and Fernando. He is a radical and is, in fact, the most original of our poets in English. His genius resides in his ability to unite Western and Sinhalese traditions in his poetry and in his ability to express himself freely as a Sri Lankan. These are exemplified obviously in the violent denunciation of imperialist exploitation through the guise of art in 'Don't Talk to Me about Matisse'. These are abilities that belong to a major writer in the Sri Lankan context and Wikkramasinha made the impact of a major writer on the small world of letters (in English) in Sri Lanka. As John Wain said, 'A major artist is one who alters or modifies the tradition of his art. A minor artist may be exquisite, and give great pleasure, and be remembered with much honour and gratiude, without affecting the way his art is practised or thought of.'[12]

Anne Ranasinghe's origins are Western—a Jew, she fled the pogroms in Germany just before the beginning of the Second World War—but her poetry is much less influenced by Western tradition than Fernando's or Gooneratne's and she writes in a freer, personal way. She is different from Wikkramasinha too. She does not know well either of the two languages of Sri Lanka, is not in touch with indigenous traditions, and is altogether of a cast of mind different from native Sri Lankan poets. Her strength as a poet comes about when she relives the past in the present, when she connects her experience of the Nazi massacres with an immediate experience.

Jean Arasanayagam is a member of the Burgher community (that is, of mixed Dutch and native descent), the most Westernized and smallest community in Sri Lanka, very different from the mass of the people, but she married a Tamil and identifies herself with her husband's community. Her poetry brings us to the immediate present. 'A Country at War' is more restrained and more complex than her earlier efforts to present the ethnic crisis in Sri Lanka—her major preoccupation in recent years.

Reggie Siriwardena is a remarkable man of letters who has recently begun writing original poetry, his technique benefiting from his earlier successful efforts of translating poetry from several languages and striving 'to be faithful to the principles of brevity, lucidity and form' learnt from the great Russian poet, Anna Akhmatova.[13] He reveals his sensitivity to the tragic situation in which the country, and indeed civilization, is placed in our violent era in 'Waiting for the Soldier' and 'Report from the Front', which reflect his love of Pushkin's style, both in the fine balancing of freedom and formal grace and in the equipoise of seriousness and wit.

*

The nationalist currents of the 1950s had a direct and positive impact on the Sinhalese cultural scene: 1956 saw the appearance of Lester James Peiris' *Rekawa*, a film which marked a decisive break from South Indian cinema and heralded a serious, distinctively Sri Lankan, idiom; Ediriwira Sarachchandra's stylized play *Maname* ushered in a new era in Sinhalese drama;

and Martin Wickremasinghe's novel *Viragaya* (Freedom from Passion) stressed the complexities of the individual character, which pioneered a new trend in Sinhalese fiction. This cluster of works signalled the beginning of a cultural reawakening.

The origins of prose in Sinhalese, however, go as far back as the third century B.C. when Buddhism was introduced into Sri Lanka from India. One surmises that the literature would have related to the religion, but it has not survived. The earliest extant prose works of importance date from the thirteenth century and were pietistic—the *Amavatura* of Gurulugomi, the *Butsarana* of Vidyachakravarti. These tales and others like the *Jataka* tales (stories of the past lives of Buddha), which were recorded in the fourteenth century and were popularized by monks who used them to illustrate their sermons, formed part of a popular oral tradition. It was supplemented by a rich tradition of folk tales, stories dealing with the *gamarala* (the farmer) and the *gamamahage* (the farmer's wife) and with the *mahadanamutta* (the great, old, wise man), handed down from one generation to the next, providing entertainment and homely wisdom.

There was a long hiatus in the prose tradition from the fifteenth to the mid-nineteenth centuries owing to colonial domination and the consequent low status of Sinhalese; the little work done was authored by monks and scholars and was not secular or popular in character. When Sinhalese fiction arose at the turn of this century, it did so under the influence partly of the popular oral literary tradition, which contained the rudiments of fiction, and partly of foreign (mainly British) literature. Among the earliest fictional works were translations of *Pilgrim's Progress* (1885), *Gulliver's Travels* (1888) and *The Arabian Nights* (1894). The immediate stimulus for the rise of fiction was provided by intellectual activity in the mid-nineteenth century when there was spirited debate in prose in magazines, journals and newspapers over religious, social and literary issues. In fact, the first attempts at fiction were offshoots of it. L. Issac D. Silva, a Christian, was the first to publish original long fiction. His two stories, *Vasanavanta Pavula* (The Fortunate Family) and *Kalakanni Pavula* (The Miserable Family) were first serialized in the Christian journal *Ruvan Maldama* beginning in 1886 and published in book form in 1888 by The Ceylon Religious Tract Society. Piyadasa Sirisena, the leading Buddhist writer of fiction in this period, wrote his first novel, *Vasanavanta Vivahaya* (The

Fortunate Marriage), in 1906 as a challenge to the earlier work of Issac D. Silva of the Christian faction.

Sirisena, who wrote over fifteen novels, used his fiction as an arm of the national and religious revivalist movements of his day. It was didactic and moralistic. On the other hand, the fiction of W. A. Silva, the other leading contemporary Sinhalese writer, was sentimental and romantic. Both seem to have been influenced by the popular and inconsequential type of romantic writing in England represented by Marie Corelli and Ethel M. Dell. Sirisena and Silva opened up popular veins of writing. They did not provide Sinhalese fiction with a good beginning but their work was not without its usefulness. They helped to establish fiction as a genre, at least providing samples from which serious practitioners could depart or refine, and secure a reading public among the middle class.

In fact, the early works of Martin Wickremasinghe, the first Sinhalese fiction writer of distinction, resembled those of Piyadasa Sirisena. His novel, *Gamperaliya* (The Changing Village), published in 1944, however, marks a turning point in his career and is a landmark in the history of the Sinhalese novel. It expresses an essentially Sinhalese sensibility with imagination and truth in a realistic form. The process of social change depicted in *Gamperaliya* became the subject of a trilogy.

*

Wickremasinghe, in the course of his long life, ventured into diverse fields—the novel, short story, drama, philosophy and criticism. His first work was published in 1914, his last in 1975, and he was long acknowledged as the doyen of Sinhalese letters. I have not included any of the over hundred stories written by him because almost all were written before Independence, and though historically valuable for introducing Chekovian realism, are period pieces.

The paths blazed by Wickremasinghe were explored and extended by writers such as Ediriwira Sarachchandra, Gunadasa Amerasekera and Simon Navagattegama. Ameresakera gained notoriety in the late 1950s for frankly presenting, probably under the influence of D. H. Lawrence, unconventional sexual experiences (adulterous liaisons and liaisons with prostitutes) in his novels *Karumakkarayo*—The Wretched Ones (1955), and *Yali*

Upannemi—I Was Born Again (1958), but it was important to widen the range of themes available to Sinhalese writers, especially in the central area of sexual experiences where centuries-old inhibitions and taboos operate. Karuna Perera, in 'A Light in the Darkness' (1971), is able to gain complexity and subtlety by suggesting that the mother in the story is compelled to supplement her meagre income by engaging in prostitution. Perera herself helps to expand the frontiers of fiction by dealing with the city working class which, earlier, has figured little in Sri Lankan literature. The symbolism of light and darkness in the story shows how contemporary Sinhalese writers too are exploiting in fiction resources usually associated with poetry.

Much of Sinhalese fiction contemplates the conflict between Eastern and Western culture as it manifested itself in contemporary Sri Lanka. In 'Disonchinahamy', Gunadasa Amerasekera presents a many-sided and critical impression of this conflict. The English-educated doctor finds himself an alien in England as well as in Sri Lanka. There are gulfs between different classes in the same community—between the English-educated doctor and his clerk, who is Sinhalese-educated; and also lower down the social ladder, between the doctor, on the one hand, and Disonchinahamy and her husband, who are rural and uneducated, on the other (the doctor cannot understand that the husband's demonstrative expression of grief is perfectly natural to one of his type and that so is Disonchinahamy's reticence). The author reveals the doctor as being exceptionally liberal and concerned about his unprivileged patients, but as having a blind side too.

The mantle of Martin Wickremasinghe has now fallen upon Ediriwira Sarachchandra, who is, in fact, even more versatile. He is the leading novelist in English as well. It is particularly apposite that he is being represented by the story 'Of a Queen and a Courtesan', because he is the pioneering and foremost playwright in Sinhalese and is one who directs the production of his own plays. The subject of the story is uncommon—the interaction of art and life and the complications that arise from it, especially when the boundary between the two is blurred.

The Sinhalese language is 'diglossic'. There is a marked gap between its written and spoken forms. The lexico-grammatical system of written Sinhalese with its Sankritized vocabulary and elaborate inflectional endings for number, case, person and gender is strikingly different from that of spoken Sinhalese with its mixed vocabulary derived from diverse sources, non-classical (Tamil, English, Portuguese, Dutch, Malay) as well as classical (Sanskrit, Poli) and its limited case and concord relations. The use of the language in polemic and controversy in the latter half of the nineteenth century revivified prose and somewhat reduced the gap. When, in 1956, Sinhalese was installed as the official language and became the medium of education in schools and universities for those to whom it was the mother tongue, the new pressures on the language resulted both in an extension of its capacity and in a further reduction of the gap. This is revealed, in a heightened form, in the works of contemporary writers such as Amerasekera and Sarachchandra, while the colloquialization of written Sinhalese is taken further by younger writers like Simon Navagattegama.

Sri Lanka is still largely rural, non-industrial and Sinhalese speaking, and this kind of milieu naturally predominates in the literature in Sinhalese. When artists like Navagattegama, in 'The Addict', write of it, they do so with a familiarity, authority and richness of detail which their counterparts in English cannot quite muster. His portrayal is supremely realistic, complex, and also ultimately life-enhancing and positive. He does focus on poverty, squalor and drunkenness; *kasippu*, an illicit brew, is the drink of the poorest. Sadana's happiness is blighted when his wife contracts a serious disease, but tenderness survives although it appears to have been dissipated by the endless vituperation of the suffering invalid and the discomfort of her husband who shrinks away to the refuge offered by absence or rotgut. 'Cortal' David, the thriving illicit brewer, is shrewd, yet not exploitative. The free drink he gives Sadana after he has forfeited his mortgage, reveals a rudimentary sense of fair play, as does the fact that he delays taking possession of Sadana's house and property and offers Sadana an alternative shelter when he does.

The short story in Sinhalese captures areas of experience different from that in English, yet it is still at a developmental stage. But in the field of poetry, we have had a history of lively interest and experimentation from early times. The eighth to tenth century verse epigrams scratched on the Mirror Wall of King Kasyapa's rock fortress of Sigiriya by later visitors still survive. There is a long tradition of folk poetry—much of it not even printed as yet—which is still to be evaluated. It influenced the narrative and erotic poetry of the seventeenth and eighteenth centuries. In the mid-eighteenth century, thanks to the efforts of the monk Velivita Saranankara, there was a notable revival of the classical tradition in literature. It completely disappeared when the entire island came under British rule in 1815 and official support for Buddhism and the Sinhalese culture ceased.

In the first half of the twentieth century, under the influence of Western (especially English) writers, imitative poems were written. The atmosphere of the time affected poetry too and there arose crude, propagandistic and nationalistic verse. Munidasa Cumaratunga made an attempt to revivify Sinhalese literature by going back to 'pure' Sinhalese or the Elu language, that is, the language as it existed prior to the Sanskritization of the post-tenth century writers. He did not succeed, but the cause still has its adherents.

The 1950s saw the beginnings of significant developments in Sinhalese poetry. The University of Ceylon at Peradeniya provided a potent stimulus to creativity in the field of Sinhalese letters. There emerged a bilingual educated class which appreciated the best in Western cultural traditions and sought to combine the West and the East in Sinhalese writing. Siri Gunasinghe and Gunadasa Amerasekera are the best exponents of this blending. They belong to a group designated the Peradeniya poets, which centred around the University. They were also dubbed the *Nisandas* (Free Verse) poets since they experimented with *vers libre*. The *Gi* and earlier types of verse compositions which are unrhymed and show considerable freedom in point of metre, had given way to the monorhyme quatrain, which had become the accepted convention. The *Nisandas* poets were thus innovators. They were opposed and criticized by their non-academic rivals centred around the metropolis, the Colombo poets. The modernist language, poetic freedom and disenchantment of Gunasinghe's 'Dirty Dishwater' are characteristic of his school of poetry. On the other hand, Gunadasa Amerasekera's 'Darkness That Calls Forth Demons' gains unselfconsciousness and immediacy because he draws on common folk belief; remorse, conflict, unease that torment and devour, take terrifying but familiar shape. In 'A Poem on the Moon', Wimal Dissanayake, a younger product of the University at Peradeniya, draws on the same thing to make a kind of pronouncement on life, to express a credo, where the horror of life and inevitablility of death coexist with the immutable fact of beauty. The moon recurs in Mahagama Sekera's 'Moon and New York City' (1970), not as a symbol of beauty, but as the one familiar face in his desperate nostalgia for his village.

With poetic and linguistic controversies and issues behind them, the poets of the 1970s and after could engage whole-heartedly in poetry as such, yet the atmosphere of the time—the insurrection of 1971; the demand for 'relevance' in drama and literature, crudely formulated or not—pressed them to contemplate social and political problems. 'Piyasena's Question' reflects Monica Ruwanpathirana's constant concern with inequality, while Parakrama Kodituwakku's 'Court Inquiry of a Revolutionary' and 'An Unfinished Lesson' deal with its consequences. But the individual too has a place. Thilakaratna Kuruvita Bandara's 'Premadasa—Pity and Rage' is an expression of personal loneliness and frustration. The poets build upon the skills of their predecessors. In 'Court Inquiry of a Revolutionary', Kodituwakku cunningly puts the sections of the poem in language appropriate to its speaker. The speakers of sections I, II, III and IV make statements, while the accused of section V speaks in a poetic language, rich in metaphor, showing with whom the author's own sympathies lie.

The literature in English is continuing to proliferate, but Ediriwira Sarachchandra feels that the arts in Sinhalese are in a state of flux, unable to withstand 'the (recent) flood of commercialism and an avalanche of cheap popular culture from the industrialised countries of the West'.[14] Perhaps it is too early to come to conclusions.

*

The winds of change of the 1950s made a deep impact on Tamil writing too, and brought about a Tamil literature which was different from that in South India and possessed a distinctively Sri Lankan identity. The South Indian film and dance forms like Bharata Natyam, Kathak and Kathakali continued to exert a stranglehold on Tamil mass entertainment and art in Sri Lanka, but fiction, poetry and drama broke loose.

Under the shadow of South India, a Sri Lankan Tamil literature was unable to emerge until the seventeenth century.

As puristic scholars on both sides of the Palk Strait endeavoured to follow a South Indian and Sanskrit tradition, the first Sri Lankan Tamil literary works were written in a religious spirit, confined to commentaries on the ancient classics, tedious and conventional. The first spark occurred in the late nineteenth century as a consequence of religious zeal and conflict. Christian missionaries sought to proselytize by preaching in the native language, and they enlisted traditional poetic forms to express Christian themes. On the other hand, to combat the inroads of missionaries, Hindu poets created works which explicated and exalted their own religion. This literature too was of a didactic sort. With the spread of English education, there were faltering attempts by the Tamils to imitate Western models.

The 1950s saw Tamil writing becoming irrevocably secular and popular in character. The Tamils in the north of Sri Lanka are different in many ways from the Tamils along the east coast, and both are very different from the Tamils of the hill country who were originally brought across from India by the British in colonial times to work on their plantations as indentured labourers. Each region has its own dialect, myths and legends. In recent years, there has occurred a radicalization of Tamil politics, the cry for a separate state for the Tamils, virtual civil war in the North and the East until lately, and the simmering aftermath. Women have stood alongside men on the battlefield and in the streets, and this will create a lasting change in gender relations in what was earlier an ultra-patriarchal society. To express these complex and formidable realities in literature is a difficult and an ongoing process, and serious Tamil writers have been notable for showing a social consciousness and responsibility in this regard.

In 'Funeral Pyre' (1960), P. Thambirajah reveals both social conscience and skill as he depicts the cruelties of the caste system. He is so liberal as to make an untouchable, Moopan, a tom-tom beater, his central character. Interestingly, in this story, the folk who belong to a depressed class, are artists who take pride in their skill. Moopan's dream is to have his pupils drum their best at his funeral. Thambirajah's sympathy for Moopan's plight is both stiffened and intensified by the irony that he, who beats tom-toms at others' funerals, cannot have them beaten at his own, recalling the situation in Alagu Subramanium's story in English of 'Professional Mourners' who were compelled to mourn at another's funeral instead of at their own mother's.

K. Saddanathan's 'Vimala' (1979) is written almost two decades after Thambirajah's story. He shows the same kind of society in the North, but as changing, though slowly and painfully: women emancipating themselves and also the freer life available to Tamils outside the North and the East (in Colombo). The fact is that more than fifty per cent of the Sri Lankan Tamils live outside these regions; their kind of life is an important aspect of the Tamil experience and demands to be taken into account. Saddanathan's story is pleasant and enjoyable whereas Nandhi's 'The Spittle' is rather unpleasant, yet of interest. Its ironic perspective suggests important cultural problems underlying what appear to be petty misunderstandings and quarrels.

N.S.M. Ramaiya's 'Among the Hills' is another pleasant story, though its ending is sad. It is set among the tea plantations in the central hills and conveys potently the texture of life there despite the echoes of James Joyce's story 'Eveline'. It, too, is a study of a divided mind: the heroine is torn between her love and her family responsibilities and, as in the case of Eveline, the pull of the latter finally proves the stronger; but the whole theme is rendered in terms of a kind of milieu which is a far cry from Joyce's Dublin.

The Sri Lankan fiction writers in all three languages, English, Sinhalese and Tamil, usually write in a nineteenth-century realistic mode, reflecting the still largely traditional character of Sri Lankan society, and they are also capable of extending it in a modern spirit, incorporating the resources of poetry, allegory and streams-of-consciousness. But the good writers (except for the special case of Chitra Fernando, now resident in Australia, in her recent novella *Between Worlds*) have shown no signs of being influenced by, or arriving independently at, the post-modern artistic modes in the West. Philip Stevick is not comprehensive but his anthology *Anti-Story* suggests the range of these recent innovations. He groups his selected stories under the following categories: Against Subject—fiction in search of something to be about; Against Reality—the uses of fantasy; Against Event—the primacy of voice; Against Mimesis—fiction about fiction; Against the Middle Range of Experience—new forms of extremity; Against Analysis—the phenomenal world; Against Meaning—forms of the absurd; and Against Scale—the minimal story.[15] The post-modernists have become so disenchanted with, or alienated from, technological society that they have, in effect, made alienation the subject of their work. They have attempted to subvert, or overturn, all our received or traditional notions of what fiction is and what it is about, an expression of the state of their minds. Sri Lankans do not share this condition of mind and it is a moot point whether it is desirable or necessary to adopt or adapt Western experimental modes. Yet it is a fact that our writers have not exploited sufficiently less drastic modes and resources open to them. I observed how some of the stories I have selected employ poetic means and rise to allegorical levels. These have to be explored further. Moreover, these are not exclusively Western methods, but are found in Eastern literary traditions too. The point of view from which a story is told is another area awaiting more investigation. These seem to me the points of possible growth for our fiction.

The fresh advance made in the field of Tamil poetry in the mid-fifties by writers such as Mahakavi, R. Murugaiyan and Sillaiyoor Selvarajan, was anticipated at the turn of this century by T.A. Turaiyappapillai. In his preface to *Kitaraca Mancari,* a collection of lyrics, he wrote:

> The nature of my present work is such that I think no apology is needed for offering it to the public. I claim it to be unique, at least as far as Jaffna is concerned; for without following the beaten track of composing lyrics on personal, religious or dramatic themes, which have had, at any rate, a portion of their share of attention at far worthier hands than mine, and in spite of the thought that praising God is the noblest use to which the poetic genius can be put, my muse has preferred to sing on subjects of moral and general utility, the verses which can be used irrespective of creed. . . .

He proceeded to state that his attention was drawn 'to the great need there was in Jaffna for a number of lyrics of this kind, on subjects of social and literary interest, treated in a liberal and progressive spirit', and that there was 'a new and appreciative audience in the modern educated Jaffna which wanted a poet of modern temperament, talents and views.'[16]

Mahakavi, in 'The Chariot and the Moon', confirms the cruelties of the caste system, while in 'A Wish' he gazes steadily at the life of the Jaffna farmer and shows himself to be an uncompromising realist. R. Murugaiyan, in 'Toil', discloses the new extension of sympathies in a poem which works both on a literal and symbolic level. Social consciousness is clearer in Sillaiyoor Selvarajan's poem 'I Submit my Heart to the Salt-Giver!' in which he venerates the sea:

> for the pinch of salt you grant
> for the sparse gruel of the
> poorest man!

Selvarajan's attitude is fresh. In 'I Shall Be God', his stance recalls Shelley's position that 'poets are the unacknowledged legislators of the world.'[17] Selvarajan sees the poet as serving a communal function, as *vates*, and articulates his view in a poem that possesses a logical development of ideas and shape. Kurunji Nathan's 'Where is Justice? Here We Go. . .' presents a view of the plantation Tamils, a reluctance to be repatriated to the unknown South India despite hardships in Sri Lanka.

M. A. Nuhman belongs to the group of younger Tamil poets which also includes S. Maunaguru, V. Kantavanam and Puthuvai Ratnadurai. They have popularized public readings of poetry and often address themselves to the most urgent issues of the immediate present—national and international. In 'Our Grandpa had an Elephant', through images, Nuhman conveys an account of the rise, decline and resurgence of Islam and calls upon the working class to awaken to the fact that it has been exploited and to claim its rights. He alludes to how learning came to medieval Europe via the Arabs. According to the most recent census (1981), the population of Sri Lanka is over 15 million, comprising 73.98 per cent Sinhalese, 12.6 per cent Tamils, 7.12 per cent Moors, 5.56 per cent Indian Tamils, 0.29 per cent Malays, 0.26 per cent Burghers and 0.20 per cent others. The Muslims form an important minority. In 'Murder', Nuhman ponders the ethnic crisis and suggests how religion becomes a casualty in this type of violence.

*

In selecting stories and poems for this anthology, I have included those by writers with established reputations as well as those by less professional writers when these are of importance and interest. In regard to the selections from the literature in Sinhalese and Tamil, we must bear in mind the limitations of translations and the necessity for them. I have been hampered by the dearth of translations. All in all, the growth of Sri Lankan literature in the last four decades is remarkable: the period is an extremely short span when viewed in terms of a literary tradition of a nation.

September 1991   D.C.R.A. GOONETILLEKE
Kelaniya, Sri Lanka

Notes to Introduction

1. Frantz Fanon, *The Wretched of the Earth*, Penguin, London, 1967 edn, pp. 26, 57, 74.

2. Yasmine Gooneratne, 'New Fiction', in *New Ceylon Writing*, 1979, p. lll

3. David Carroll, *Chinua Achebe*, Macmillan, London, 1980, p. 23.

4. Lakdasa Wikkramasinha, 'Note', in *Lustre: Poems*, Ariya, Kandy, 1965, p. 51.

5. T.S. Eliot,'The Social Function of Poetry', in *On Poetry and Poets*, Faber, London, 1971 edn, pp. 19, 22.

6. W. B. Yeats, 'Discoveries', in *Essays and Introductions*, Macmillan, London, 1961, p. 266.

7. F.R. Leavis, *Revaluation*, Chatto & Windus, London, 1953, p. 11.

8. F.R. Leavis, *New Bearings in English Poetry*, Chatto & Windus, London, 1942, p. 42.

9. T. Kandiah, 'New Ceylon English', in *New Ceylon Writing*, 1971, p. 92.

10. Ibid, p. 91.

11. Biodun Jeyifo, 'Soyinka at 50', in *West Africa*, August 27, 1984, pp. 1730, 1731.

12. John Wain, 'The Importance of Philip Larkin', in *The American Scholar*, Summer 1986, p. 351.

13. Reggie Siriwardena, 'Preface' to the *Muse of Insomnia*, privately published, Colombo, 1990, p. 1.

14. Ediriwira Sarachchandra, 'Development and Traditional Values, Moral and Aesthetic', The Punithan Tiruchelvam Memorial Lecture 1989, Sri Lanka Tamil Women's Union, p. 10.

15. Philip Stevick, ed. *Anti-Story: An Anthology of Experimental Fiction*, The Free Press, New York, 1971, pp. vi-vii.

16. Quoted from K.Kailasapathy, 'A Century of Tamil Poetry in Sri Lanka: An Introductory Note', in *Journal of South Asian Literature*, Vol. 22, No. 1, 1987, p. 123.

17. Shelley, 'A Defence of Poetry,' quoted from *Prose of the Romantic Movement*, ed: John R. Nabholtz, Macmillan, New York, 1974, p. 738.

Part I

Writing in English

Godfrey Gunatillake

The Garden

Tissa turned the damp earth with the digging fork, cautiously avoiding the young plant. He was squatting beside the bed of coleus, his sarong stretched neatly without one wrinkle over the clear rotundity of his hips. His bare back was glistening in the pale evening sun. Methodically he plucked out the weeds and stopped occasionally to loosen the earth, sieving with his fingers the large round pebbles in the soil. An earthworm crawled underneath a clod and Tissa inclined his head a little to watch it as its moist pink nudity shrank and grew in its efforts to get under the earth. He was working leisurely, without strain; the whole evening was before him. In the measured movement of his hands, this placid attendance on his garden, there was a rich deliberation, as though he were consciously savouring his leisure. For this was not just gardening for him, mere occupation for his spare hours. The way he moved and worked with unhurried pleasure was like a ritual in which he found expression for the unstirred composure of his being, the windlessness within which the long hours slowly passed for him now. The days and nights came and went with their familiar comfort.

He turned round to look for the cattle-dung which Jamis, his servant, had brought. A tiny leap heap lay beside the bed—a few mouldy cakes and a handful of grey green powder. 'James!' he shouted, 'is this all the manure? The lazy beggar,' he muttered under his breath casually spreading the heap. A little beetle scrambled and rolled away like a bright iridescent bead. 'Coming, *mahattaya**,' the servant called back, 'I am bringing more.'

Tissa stood up, with his soiled hands hanging loosely, carefully held away from the sarong. He was a steady, well set man,

---

* gentleman

about thirty-five years old. His broad fleshy face was variously marked with minute scars and pits, the ruins, left behind by innumerable pimples which had plagued his youth. But his eyes gave a hint of his smile, a smile which with the faintest provocation broadened into a grin, bright like a sickle moon right across his face, lightening the face with a sense of humour and making him instantly likeable. His close-cropped hair was already flecked with a light grey, which accorded with the large-limbed mildness and good humour he diffused. His eyes were a subdued brown, and when he spoke one detected a scarcely audible lisp which reinforced the impression of innocence and ineffectuality which flawed his big-boned reliability.

Across the door Tissa could see his wife. She had stopped for a while in the act of sweeping, to watch Tissa at his work. She had bathed earlier in the day, and her long black hair hung loose, in bedraggled wet strands, below her slim waist. With one foot poised lightly on the broom, and the handle held firmly under her chin, she was gazing at him, half-pensive, half-amused. 'Everything must be brought to the foot of the lord and master,' she said teasingly. 'Why don't you shake that lazy body of yours a little more and bring the manure yourself?'

'Yes, won't you like to see me work, you hussy,' he answered affectionately. 'Do you know while you were bathing, I prepared four excellent beds? In two months you will have a garden which will be the envy of the entire neighbourhood,' he finished in his deliberate drawl.

'You wait,' Prema replied, 'I'll finish sweeping and come out to see you work. I am sure it will have to be redone.'

Jamis, a squint-eyed boy of seventeen, had come into the garden with a pan full of the cattle dung and ash. His round face permanently wore a comical inquisitive expression; the features appeared as though they had been cast in a soft and malleable material which, with a little pressure, had been flattened and blunted out of its originally sharp lines. He sat down beside the bed of coleus, pulverized a cake of dung with his fingers, and mixing it with ash, scattered it carefully over the bed.

Tissa stood by watching him as he went from bed to bed lightly spreading the manure. 'Let Jamis do it,' he thought indolently, raising his arm to brush aside two little streams of months. Prema had once been his little cousin, fifteen years younger than he, and now she was his wife. At the age of thirty-five he was married and had a home of his own. Who would have guessed it? At one time he could have seen no conclusion to his own life with his mother, his brothers and his sisters. When his father had died it had fallen to him at the age of seventeen to seek employment and earn for the family. Then there had been the interminable relay of duties seeing that his sisters got married, sending his brothers to school, caring for his constantly ailing mother, redeeming the mortgage on their house, ensuring that this was done and preventing that from happening, all this. All this and much more. But of course that endless drift of days had brought for him a sense of importance, a sense of having accomplished what was needed. At that time who would have thought, indeed, that this was the life in store for him?

Prema's brother had told him that Prema had been reluctant at first, and had to be gently persuaded to marry him—'gently' Prema's brother had emphasized with a smile. When his mother had first proposed the marriage, Prema, it appeared, had received it with embarrassed astonishment. He recalled how, when they had returned home after their honeymoon, he had taxed her with her reluctance. There had been an amused twinkle in her eyes: 'Why, you know, I thought it would be like living with my elder brother,' she replied. 'In fact I cannot still refrain from calling you Tissa *Aiya**.' Tissa and Prema's elder brother, Gamini, were of the same age, and were intimate friends. 'But you are such a sweet man, so affectionate, Tissa, I like you very much,' she concluded, hugging him close to her without a trace of self-consciousness as she would have embraced a person much older or younger than herself. At that moment he had felt an indefinable distress, a strange tightening inside him as when in his childhood he had been on the verge of tears. He had remained silent, attending to that momentary, inaudible pain inside him, his eyes unthinkingly fixed on the bright multi-coloured dance of moths in a little shaft of sunlight which had entered through the grill over the window. Prema had meanwhile left his arms and was looking with pleasure at her new home, the inexpensive but tasteful furniture in the sitting-room, the dainty hangings with their delicate prints of a creeper with large light blue flowers, which she herself had selected. . . . Tissa waved the memory aside as being of little consequence.

---

* Elder Brother

Their house was situated on top of a little hillock, along a gravelled path. The garden was neatly enclosed with a railing of galvanized iron pipes on which Prema would lean in the evenings, peering out intermittently, watching for his return from the office. It was a small house tidily laid out and pleasing to the eye. The windows were draped with light blue curtains, the doors and windows newly painted in a light cream, and the walls distempered afresh. From without, the entire house had the faint suggestion of an idyll. Within, the house had a spruce, spacious look; the few pieces of furniture gave it a deceptive look of spaciousness. In the sitting-room there was a settee with two comfortable chairs, upholstered in a soft russet cretonne, and a centre table, on which stood an earthenware vase, a wedding gift. Their living-room was furnished with two teak beds, a dressing-table, and a compact wardrobe. Prema took special care to see that the vase was always fully laden with the roses and the chrysanthemums from their garden, roses not large and crimson, but the medium-sized ones, their petals lit by a faint flush, and chrysanthemums, white, with a trace of gold in their hearts. In the dining-room over the door which led to the kitchen was a large picture of the Buddha in meditation, a soft benign Buddha who smiled tenderly, with a tint of rose in his cheeks. Tissa had not yet been able to purchase a dining-table but they managed with a slightly rickety four-legged table which Prema had collected from her mother. Yes, Tissa told himself, Prema had turned it into a cosy home. It was a house which might belong to any not-very-well-to-do middle-class family in Ceylon, but his wife had imparted to it something of her own small elegant self. Everything in it had the look of what had been diminished from its original dimension, pretty and petite, like an apt composition round Prema—his good-looking wife and cousin. All its colours had a sweet convalescent shade, nowhere did the eye encounter the bright disturbance of a living hue.

Jamis had finished manuring the beds and had left the garden. Tissa went from bed to bed, straightening a stem here, plucking a weed there, waiting impatiently till his wife joined him. His neighbour was taking his daily bath. He listened awhile to the long-drawn metallic screech of the pulley, the soft splash of water on limbs, the intermittent splutter and loud cough which followed. It went on and on, with a regular monotone. Prema came into the garden. She was now wearing her hair in a thick, loosely woven plait. It was late evening and the sun was gentle amidst the lengthening shadows. A shower earlier in the day had left behind a subdued washed sky, with smoothed-out wisps of cloud. In the west, the colour flowed like honey where the sky met the smudged margin of trees, but in the east where the light was fading, an aqueous blue paled gradually into a white trans-lucence. There was a refreshing hint of moisture in the air. A light wind blew now and again, and the dried leaves of the jak tree which spread over the garden fell one by one, with a soft rustle littering the beds. 'This darned jak tree,' Prema said, 'you clean, and clean but the leaves keep on falling.'

'Let the me see your beds,' she said turning to Tissa. Tissa proudly led her round.

'Oh, you baby!' she cried, 'I didn't want you to have a bed there close to the railing; the neighbours' goats put in their heads through the railing. And then a fat lot of flowers you will get.'

Tissa looked crestfallen, and then with mock distress: 'Nothing will please my mistress. What shall I do?' he asked,wringing his hands.

Prema laughed. 'But don't you see, dear one, that there is a very simple solution. You just have to plant a few stakes there alongside the railing.'

'Oh rare, rare genius,' Tissa exclaimed, 'wait, I'll bring the packet of seeds.'

'What are you planting here?' she asked.

'Verbenas, as you suggested.'

'Wouldn't it be a sweet little garden? Isn't it very nice the way I planned it?' Prema inquired.

Tissa looked round. Even now, with the few flowers there were, it had an orderliness, a dainty consonance from colour to colour that was a delight to the eye. Beds of coleus, a rich dis-array of colour, wine spilt on green or a wild melee of cream and purple. Rose bushes in two beds, planted according to their colours—in one few flowers large and dark red, like bright new wounds between the finely cut leaves, in the other, a host of delicate pink-complexioned roses. The large white chrysanthe-mums, drooping in a corner, over limp leaves, like soft spools too heavy for the stems which supported them; and against them the marigolds, with their thousand crenellated petals, not the flaming orange, but a light butter yellow which seemed to melt to the sight. On either side of the house was a long rectangular wooden trough—begonias, with a profusion of flowers which hung over the red-green frowning leaves like a pale pink mist. These and other varieties, all arranged according to their kind and colour without a discomforting hint of nature's wildness. The eye was restful and the heart complacent in Prema's garden.

'Not bad,' Tissa answered, as he turned to go into the house.

'You buffalo,' Prema cried, simulating anger, 'are you going into the house like that, with your feet caked with mud? I have just cleaned it and swept the floor.'

'Dear, dear,' Tissa answered, 'I am like the beast in the beauty's parlour, am I not?' and making a wry face he rubbed his feet vigorously on the rough granulated plinth, and wiped it clean on the doormat before going in. When he went in he called for Prema.

'What is it, pet?' Prema asked as she walked in. 'Now I've got you,' Tissa replied slipping in between her and the door. He spread out his hands which were all grimed with earth and cattle-dung, and with a mischievous smile on his face, made passes at her as though he intended to wipe his hands on her. Prema shrieked, dodging his hands and turning to run away, but he circled round her and brought his soiled hands within an inch of her face. And then, swiftly, holding away his palms so that they wouldn't soil her, he took her into his arms and carried her to the settee. With his legs and arms he entwined her close to him so that she had no choice but to lie on his body and be kissed again and again. When he let her go, she smiled at him, half-affectionately, half-petulantly. Without being quite aware of it, she took deep pleasure in the affection which he revealed to her in the unexpected caress, the sudden endearment which would interrupt her daily routine.

'No, I am not pleased with you, Tissa,' she said wiping her face with the sleeve of her jacket. 'I had washed my face and made up for the evening, and now you have dishevelled me again. See your chest, all wet with perspiration. You will have to take a body wash, you pig,' she said wrinkling her nose. He smiled, studying her face as she spoke. All her features were gathered up into a small oval, but every feature was delicately delineated, and when she came close, one felt that she was decidedly pretty. There was a submissive grace about her form, it resided unmistakably in her large brown eyes, the eyes of an animal which would be easily frightened. But her mouth, small and full, formed naturally into a pout, which at times revealed her as a stubborn and selfish child.

'Never mind your being dishevelled, bring me a glass of water,' Tissa said. 'I am very thirsty, woman.'

She promptly went into the kitchen and brought him a glass of water which she held out to him to drink. As he drank it slowly, he watched her. He was comfortable and happy, yes, comfortable and happy, he told himself. His body, a very dark muscular body, glowed with a sense of well-being, as after a good satisfying meal, not too rich, not too delicious, He never dreamt in his bachelor days that he would be fond of a woman as he was of this girl Prema, his wife. His cousin, the small creature, who looked so lovely and vulnerable, had filled his life with a new tenderness. The extravagance of romantic love read about in books or seen in films had always bewildered him: he had never been convinced by it. Yet his affection for this woman, without any deep perturbation of the spirit, the familiar fondness for the known thing, had grown during the last few months after his marriage into the central thing in his life, so that, in the evenings, when he went shopping, he would avoid buying beans or pumpkin, because Prema did not eat them. He would try to hurry home to have as much time with her as he could. He was always aware of her consciously as of one very much younger to him, known to him all her life, very familiar and lovable. The little girl whom he had petted at the age when she would unselfconsciously prance about without clothes, had become his wife. Her acceptance of him made him very kindly towards her and deeply protective. Even in the darkness of night, in the dreaded extremity of physical passion, when they were revealed, did not a strange compassionate distraction come over him as she clung to him with a trembling body? Then he would caress her with a tenderness mingled with a vague undefined pity.

As he gave her the glass, Tissa paused awhile to dwell on a memory which had come to him upon seeing her wipe her face with the sleeve of her jacket, and standing beside him with the empty glass. It was at Nuwara Eliya during their honeymoon. He had finished his afternoon meal. He remembered he had not drunk any water during the meal, though he had been thirsty. He always enjoyed slaking his thirst after the meal with a long uninterrupted draught. One glass had not been sufficient. He had reached for the glass beside Prema and drunk half of it. Prema had finished eating and remarked with a trace of irritation in her voice, 'I am thirsty.' She had tapped testily on the table for the waiter. Tissa had asked, 'Why don't you drink that water till he brings you more?' The water had been iced, and the glass was misty with moisture. She screwed up her face with mild distaste and pointed to the neat curve impressed on the moist glass; there was a faint, almost imperceptible, trace of grease where his lips had rested. 'I find it difficult to drink out of a glass from which someone else has drunk,' she said apologetically. Yes, that was the first occasion he had felt that dim intangible pain very far inside him.

'Why do you have that silly far-away look?' Prema asked him when she came back, after leaving the glass on the plate rack. 'What are you thinking?'

'Oh,' he answered evasively, 'I was thinking how fond I was of you.'

She laughed, her voice vibrant with pleasure. 'What are you doing tomorrow?' she asked him, 'I know that it is a public holiday.'

'Oh what a bore! I thought it would be a nice surprise for you early tomorrow morning when I stretched and yawned and said to you casually, "I am not going to office today." '

'Well, don't be so upset, you can take me home for the day.'

He got sorely disappointed, listening to her. He had planned to spend the entire day together with her, but she wanted to go 'home' as though she lived elsewhere in some temporary lodging and had her permanent home with her parents.

As he got up from the settee, Tissa remembered why he had come into the house. 'Prema, I called you, at first, to take out the packet of seeds from the wardrobe. I couldn't with my hands.'

Before they went out into the garden, Prema stepped behind the door and held Tissa close to her. How warm and protective his big body seemed. She was content to have him, this neat orderly house, the affectionate security he gave her, and the newly acquired importance as the mistress of her home. She held up her face to be kissed and brought her limbs close, very close, to his, so that in that large warm body which encompassed her, she might forget. . . what? she wondered. Not something which lay in her past for there was nothing there; then forget perhaps, some indefinite weight of a dream which she may have dreamed for her future? He bent down and kissed her. As he stepped out into the garden he wondered how his mother and her brothers would view their life together. He was almost shy of their tenderness. Her brothers would, of course, laugh teasingly at Prema, and his mother with crude traditional wisdom would say, 'The appetite grows with tasting.' He was undeniably happy, he told himself. What was it? Like the vessel brimming with curd and honey. . . curd and honey, that was the likeness of their life. Hand in hand they went to the corner of the garden where the new bed had been prepared.

It was a triangular bed wedged between two sides of the railing. He broadcast the seeds and scattered earth over them. Then collecting a few sticks he thought he would plant them alongside the railing as Prema had suggested. Gingerly he stretched a leg over the bed, without trampling it, and jumped to the other side. There was little space between the railing and bed and seated awkwardly with much discomfort he completed his task.

Prema meanwhile was walking about the garden admiring their joint handiwork. It was nearly dark and the pictorial loveliness of the garden in daytime was mitigated by the indifferent sombre light. The flowers hid their colours and seemed to withdraw before the night. The plantain trees in the next garden were lovelier—the leaves swayed from side to side in the wind, the bottle-green alternating with the pale velvet of the undersides, the last light scattering and slipping with a dim mercurial glow on their broad fans. After the warm day, it was very cool, and it gave Prema much pleasure to walk about, while her husky husband, in whose arms she would spend the night, worked at the railing in a slightly incongruous posture, driving in the stakes.

'I have finished,' he called.

'I am sure it's not well done,' she joked, from the other end of the garden.

'Are you? Come and see,' he replied.

He turned around and balanced himself precariously, holding the railing. He prepared to jump across without trampling the bed when his eyes fell on an unfamiliar colour, a strange pattern which lay stretched on the earth, on the other side of the bed. He drew in his breath and stood transfixed with surprise and fear, for a few feet away from him lay a large viper. It had stopped moving, having perhaps observed Tissa's movements.

Tissa couldn't get across without jumping over the viper. There was no other exit. Softly, with his eyes all the time on the viper, he addressed Prema: 'Prema, don't come too close, there is a viper here. I cannot get across; you would have to do something for me.'

He was watching the viper. It was beautiful, he told himself in spite of his fear, as he stared at the intricate pattern of colour on the viper's skin. The brick-red design, with its dark blotches, like bloodstains, seemed to slip and shiver on his body like silk. In the moment of danger, fantastic thoughts crowded into Tissa's mind. It seemed that the viper was also a flower, grown secretly in the garden, but more beautiful than the bright struggle of colour on the leaves of the coleus, yet unlike any flower, inaccessible, and dangerous like the nightshade.

Prema had only heard him calling her. She had not caught his words. 'Yes, my dear?' she said questioningly as she came towards him.

He warned her, 'There is a viper across the bed, and I cannot get out; don't come too close yourself.'

Prema stopped sharply. A few yards in front of her, she saw the serpent. Her eyes widened in terror, and she gave a low moan. For a moment, she was only conscious of the serpent. Everything seemed to slip and coil round that slim, terrifying shape. Her eyes darkened as with a mist, and she was convulsed with a fear she had not known all her life. With a stifled shriek, she ran inside the house.

Tissa closed his eyes; he was no longer afraid. It seemed as though an immense weight which he had carried, steeling himself all these years, had been lifted in an indivisible second, and then not relief, but the bone-destroying weariness at the futility of the effort, had descended on him. He waited leaning on the rail, indifferent and tired, watching the viper who had not yet stirred. Then he saw Jamis coming into the garden.

'Jamis!' he said, 'look at this.'

'*Amme**! *Polonga***!' he exclaimed. The incongruous mixture of alarm and nonchalance rendered him more than usually comical. He quickly reached for the mammoty which lay close to him, and from a safe distance, aimed one vicious stroke at the viper. The serpent which had been serenely and immovably patterned

---

* Mother; ** Viper

against the ground, turned in an instant into a slimy, wriggling mass. But Jamis had struck him neatly and precisely on the head and before long the viper was dead, laid out stiff and beautiful as ever.

Jamis was jubilant. He turned the viper over and over. 'What a hefty fellow,' he said, 'if he had bitten you, Mahattaya, that would have been the end.' He ran in and brought some kerosene oil. He smeared it all over the viper's body and taking it on to the road, made a little pyre with old newspapers and dried jak and coconut leaves. He placed the viper on the pyre and set fire to it. 'Ha! Ha!' he said, hopping with excitement, a strange clownish fiend, casting a weird shadow on the garden as the flames spired upwards, and the dead serpent crackled in the heat.

Tissa watched the cremation for some time, and then turned to go into the house. It was dark inside; the lamp had not yet been lit. He walked through the house, to the rear veranda, took a basin full of water and washed himself. Then he went into the kitchen to look for Prema. Alice, the cookwoman, was bending over the hearth, peering into a pot, the bottle-lamp held in one hand, high over her head, and the ladle in the other. *Nona** was not in the kitchen, she informed him grumpily, without turning around, when Tissa questioned her. He walked into the bedroom and found Prema lying on the bed with one leg crooked, and her hands crossed underneath her head, staring at the ceiling.In the dim light, her eyes were bright with an inarticulate question. She looked at him for a long time without talking. 'Tomorrow we will go home for the day, eh?' she asked softly. She spoke in Sinhalese. 'All right, Prema,' he answered in the same language. The English she spoke in their daily intercourse seemed to wrap itself lightly round her like a set of well-worn graceful clothes, but when she dropped to Sinhalese, there appeared to be a no-joking-about matter-of-factness in their relationship, recovering the old forgotten reality of their cousin-to-cousin tones, which had little in common with this that they had striven to make up, their new life.

Prema did not wish to talk to him to him of the incident in the garden. She could not understand it or herself, or anything. There with the man stretched against the rail, and the serpent

---

* Lady

which had entered her garden, something had happened which defied her understanding. How real, how decisive had been her terror she thought, clean and beyond all calculation. How could she have known that beneath her daily fondness for her man, the petty theme of endearments which she had gathered from what she knew of romantic love, the domestic preening that made up her day, that beneath all, in the inaccessible depths of her, this had lain in wait, dark and without name? But why was it, when she lay safe in bed, everything now seemed without substance—the kind man stretched by her side, silent, the neat orderly household, the pretty garden, without the serpent? Only the moment's terror, seemed her real self, her real world: there it lay like a dark and heavy stone in the clear depths of her, unmoved by the flow of the daytime consciousness which was crowding back into her again.

Disconsolate in her ruin, she felt a new pity for the man beside her, who for the first time smote her with his strangeness. She reflected comfortingly, she would be restored to her own familiar self when she went home on the morrow.

Tissa lay beside her; for a long time he could think of nothing. Again and again, he echoed a meaningless phrase, 'This was the end of his thirty-five years.' He had had a hard life for the last eighteen years after his father's death, he told himself. He had had to settle his four sisters in marriage. He had done that and at the same time maintained his younger brother while he studied at the Medical College. He was now a senior Government clerk, and at the age of thirty-five, when all his duties had been fulfilled, with a severe self-discipline, all his obligations performed with scrupulous devotion, then, he had married his nineteen-year-old cousin. And it was then, when he was accustomed to the interminable stretch, when he had found pleasure in the unpurposeful daily round, that this new tenderness had settled on him, at first untroubled and reassuring, in accord with the temperate region in which his spirit resided. There had been rare moments between the leaden hours in office and the dull distractions at home when it seemed that something else, something inexplicable had been revealed to him—while lying in bed at night when the window framed the black sky with a single star, or some other time, in the morning when he paused while brushing his teeth, to watch his neighbour's dove, lively in the air high above him and hovering for a moment like a drop of milk in the immense blue bowl of the morning sky. And it seemed that these incomprehensible stirrings in his heart, between the dust of office and the stale smells of home, had grown into the new life with Prema.

But then why had this affection become like a reluctant awak-ening, this tenderness for his wife, like an astringent spice in the cherished tastelessness of his former life? In his old life, no lone-liness had troubled him, no loss of purposes had gnawed at him. He saw Prema again in his mind's eye turning into the house with a shriek and he was filled with a bitterness he could not hold. This young person lying in bed beside him, how could he describe it, she was always under him, or in him, always. She was not extricated from his tender solicitude and placed outside him, apart from him so that he could meet her. When the serpent had appeared and had at last resolved her into another outside himself, when she had run in with a shriek, then he had been annihi-lated and without substance for her. At the time they had stood, on either side of the serpent, and the darkened flower in their pretty garden had nodded to the wind, his whole life and hers seemed revealed in the ineluctable terror of one moment—yes, but not as something illumined, only like a vision of darkness, in which the eye is plunged after the bright division of lightning.

For the first time the sense of being a stranger in his world assailed Tissa. The darkness which flowed into the room re-minded him that the lamps had not yet been lit. Rising from his bed he groped his way with an unsteady step, into the dining-hall.

Out of the growing night, suddenly a koha called, his notes cool and clear as spring water, breathlessly ascending, and then, beginning again. It startled the lonely listeners, like an immacu-late dew-drop which one surprises under a blade of grass, in the dull heat of the day.

Punyakante Wijenaike

The Third Woman

The last rays of the sun came through the open door of the hut and fell on Diyonis *Baas*'* rattan easy chair. This was the best part of the day as Diyonis *Baas* always admitted. This moment when the sun bade farewell, its gentle warmth fell like the tender soft touch of a woman's hand upon his body. He took a deep draught from the bottle in his hand. The pure, sweet scent of the white jasmine flower was strong in the compound outside. He inhaled it deep into his lungs and suddenly it seemed as if his Suduhamy was there beside him. It was a peculiar sensation. The drink and the scent of the white flower blended perfectly together though there lay a difference wide as the ocean between the two. The drink coursed through his veins like fire, making his heart beat fast. The virgin scent of the little flower uplifted him and made him feel pure and good. He closed his eyes. Suduhamy must have come back from the dead to make him feel like this again.

Diyonis *Baas* took another sip of arrack and looked sideways at Leon Singho. Leon Singho was young, yet he looked as if he had taken his liquor more easily than the older man. Diyonis *Baas* shifted his still wiry body restlessly in the armchair. Leon Singho finished his drink and belched contentedly. To him the scent of the flower meant nothing. To him there was only the task of listening. He crossed his legs and sat waiting.

Diyonis *Baas* frowned and scratched his white hair, loosening it from the tight knot at the back of his head. Then he pulled at his white moustache, squinted his bright sharp eyes at the sun, and then cleared his throat with unnecessary vigour. It was demanding a great deal of him to talk about Suduhamy but for

---

* skilled workman—in this case, a carpenter

the sake of Leon Singho he would make the sacrifice. Twenty years ago she had died and yet to talk about her was like uncovering a fresh raw wound.

'This thing called a woman must be chosen carefully by man,' admitted Diyonis *Baas* at last. 'Like the gems in Ratnapura, one must search and search without impatience. Sometimes the stone that looks pure and shining hides a crack inside. Perhaps my Suduhamy was like that. *Aiyo**, when I first saw her how could I have known that she would harbour such hatred together with the love she bore in her heart?'

Leon Singho coughed respectfully and looked away, past the door into the compound. Beyond the compound he saw the jungle, dark and frightening, for Diyonis *Baas'* hut was the last one in the row of huts which formed the small village. Sometimes, at night, Leon Singho could hear the leopard's cry from his own hut which stood four doors away from here. Only a man like Diyonis *Baas* would live so close to the jungle, unafraid.

'But it is difficult to choose so carefully when there are so few women,' grumbled Leon Singho.

Diyonis took another mouthful of the drink. It was the last in the bottle.

'That is true, and the women today are not like the women in my time. *Aiyo*, from where can one find another Suduhamy? Or another Kiri *Menike*** or Bissohamy?'

He sighed and a sudden huskiness caught at his throat.

'No, there are no women like those three,' he said in a sad voice. 'And it was my good fortune to have met them. The good deeds I did in my last birth brought me those three for comfort in this birth.'

His eyes softened as only the eyes of Diyonis *Baas* could whenever he spoke of something that touched his heart.

'My Bissohamy, now, how well I remember the first day I saw her,' said Diyonis *Baas*. 'Such a woman she was. Nobody even filled a bodice more delightfully than she. She was the wife of the *sillara kade mudalali**** who was my friend at that time. My *vadu maduva\+* was right opposite his *kade\+\+* where one morning she came to sell hoppers. That was how I came to see her. A saucy-eyed buxom creature she was, though dark in skin. But at that time I had a weakness for dark skins for I had not yet met my

---

* Alas; ** Lass; *** grocery store owner; \+ carpentry shed; \+\+ store

Suduhamy and Kiri *Menike*.

'From that moment onwards my time was pleasantly occupied in watching the tight shifting movement beneath Bissohamy's bodice. So much was I occupied that Davith *Baas*, who worked with me, began to complain that I was not doing my share of the work. At that time our work was in great demand and we were the only two carpenters of good repute. That village was not a small one like this one. It was a big village with a lot of new buildings coming up and a lot of people were in debt to us for the work we had done.

'Soon Bissohamy began to smile at me and we got to exchange a few words whenever she finished selling the hoppers or when her husband was out of the boutique. Then one day she came to me and told me that she was willing to go away with me. For a moment I was stunned. I had not thought that it would go as far as that. However I was only too glad to have her and we ran away together to her old village, to the house where her old parents lived.

'The six months that followed were among the happiest months of my life. Never before had I experienced such deep joy and fulfilment. Each night, and sometimes during the day too, my Bissohamy would lie in my arms and she would tell me:

' "Diyonis *Aiya*, without you my life is nothing."

'Then the six months ended and I had to get back to my work. I was a new man for I had tasted a woman and a woman like Bissohamy can change a man overnight. "I cannot go back to my husband," she told me calmly, "life with him now will be like eating curd without the jaggery."

'But our fears were without cause. Her husband greeted us as if nothing had happened and the six months had not been at all. Bissohamy returned to her hopper-making in the boutique and I went back to Davith *Baas* who was very glad to see me.

'Life resumed its normal course except for this one change: at night Bissohamy came to my house and cooked the evening meal and spent the night with me. It was a good sensible arrangement, for, besides getting a good tasty meal, I could not stay without my Bissohamy now. She was as necessary as food and water. Her husband approved of the new change too. For, when occasionally his *kade* needed an extra bench or a table, I would do it for him free of charge.

'And my Bissohamy brought me luck. Even Davith *Baas* was

astounded at the amount of work that came to us. Morning and evening our saws and our hammers were busy. My carpentry improved considerably with so much practice, and soon we were able to raise our charges to almost double the original amount.

'Bissohamy and I were very happy. I looked upon her as my wife though we were not married and soon everybody in the village came to accept her as that. We quarrelled heartily as a man and a woman who mean a lot to each other always do. If she was late to cook my meal, and very often she was when the *sillara kade* had a lot of business, I would shout at her impatiently and sometimes give her a good blow or two with my hand, to remind her that her duty now lay first towards me. And if I came home with the smell of drink on my lips, Bissohamy would shout and scold like a proper wife should. Yes, my Bissohamy and I were very happy. And we never thought that a change was waiting for us and so soon too.'

'I had a friend, a good friend of many years called Ran Hamy. It was he who had helped me to find a place and to set up a *vadu maduva*. It was he who had introduced me to Davith *Baas*. Through his kindness, I, a complete newcomer, had become part of that village.

'Now this man was dead. A few brief days of illness and he was gone. I was full of grief and even Bissohamy was unable to comfort me. I felt that I had not repaid Ran Hamy for the kindness he had shown me. Someday I had meant to do something for him. Something that would measure up to the depth and generosity of his own heart. But I had waited too long for the opportunity and now it would never come. I lost my appetite and could not sleep at night. I felt that I had committed a terrible crime and hampered my own chance of happiness as well. This debt would be on my head not only in this life but in the next as well. A deep feeling of ingratitude got hold of me.

'It was Davith *Baas* who roused me from my melancholy state. He pointed out that there was something that I could still do for Ran Hamy. It was not too late to repay his kindness.

'Ran Hamy's widow, Kiri *Menike*, was now alone in the house with her child, a boy of eight. When the funeral was over I went to her. She was waiting in a room, pale and drawn with grief, but otherwise her normal sweet and docile self.

' "I was very troubled when I heard of your great sorrow," I said respectfully, taking care to keep my eyes away from her face. She stood up then, very dignified and correct in her grief, her pale milk-coloured skin almost the same shade as the cloth she wore in mourning.

' "He was like a brother to me. If there is anything that has to be done, tell me and I will do it," I entreated.

'She raised her eyes, soft and gentle as a newborn calf's, while her hand trembled and strayed towards her breast. But she said nothing.

' "The house is desolate without a man. There is the boy to bring up too. Tell me if there is anything that has to be done and I will do it," I repeated. But she did not answer. She was not a woman who was made to answer. So I took the decision into my own hands and that night itself moved into Ran Hamy's house with Bissohamy.

'Now I had two women and a son and a good house to live in. Kiri *Menike* cooked a grand meal to welcome us and the feeling of guilt, of unhappiness, left my heart. I felt I had repaid Ran Hamy for all the kindness he had shown me by taking on the responsibility of his houseshold. A great burden was lifted from my shoulders. I was free to live my life unhampered.

If I had any worry about trouble in the house with two women, my fear was soon put to rest. Bissohamy and Kiri *Menike* got on well together. Where one was all hot chilly and fire, the other remained cool and sweet as the milk rice she prepared in the morning. Life went on peacefully. Bissohamy went to work daily at the *kade* and left all the cooking and cleaning to Kiri *Menike*. As for the child, he soon become the son I never had just as Kiri *Menike* his mother became my other "wife". Neither mentioned the name of Ran Hamy, even in talk, after that.'

Diyonis *Baas* paused here for a moment as if perplexed at what he was going to say next. He knitted his brows and thought heavily.

'Yes, that time was the most peaceful period in my life,' he muttered rebelliously. 'If my Suduhamy had not come, life would have gone on like a calm river. But I would not have been happy for I never wanted too much peace and calm. Forever I am a restless man.'

'Two women would have satisfied any man but I was not just any man. Bissohamy was Bissohamy and she continued to fulfil a vital need in me, and Kiri *Menike* was kind and gentle as I wanted her to be. Yet I was not wholly contented. The old restlessness began to trouble me again. The old restlessness which had kept me wandering from place to place before I came to that village and met my Bissohamy. Unconsciously I had begun the search for my Suduhamy even before I knew of her existence. I had begun to look for my real wife, the flower fate had meant to grow in my garden. But at that moment I held no picture of what I wanted. Perhaps someone who had the qualities of both my Bissohamy as well as my Kiri *Menike*, and yet different from either of them.

'Leon Singho, I do not feel like talking about this. It is like the hushed feeling one gets inside a temple on a *poya** night. One feels but cannot find the words to do justice to that feeling. But tell it I must if I am to help you. And be assured that whatever pain I suffered in the end, my Suduhamy has always remained the most precious gift the gods gave. Whatever wrong she has done has been through no fault of hers. *Aiyo*, how can you be bitter with a woman like that? One must always make excuses, tell lies to cover up for her. Because condemning her would be to condemn myself. She and I were one being. We loved each other so completely that we could not think of ourselves as two different people. So how can one be bitter against oneself?'

'About this time Kiri *Menike* began to ail from what she called "stomach trouble". She had always been a pale sickly creature and now she took to her mat and would not get up even to prepare the meals. The child did what he could to help and Bissohamy was helpless as her husband suddenly fell ill and she had to go look after him. Kiri *Menike* cried and begged me to find her a woman to help in the house.

' "A young woman, a girl who can lift and pound and sweep the place a little," she pleaded with those large timid eyes of hers. "I know of just such a girl too. An orphan, distantly related to me, who lives here in the village."

' "But who are her guardians?" I asked in astonishment. "They

---

* full moon night, holy for Buddhists

might not like to give the girl to me, seeing that I am a low country man. And besides another woman in the house would only lead to trouble."

' "If you speak to the girl she will come of her own accord," said Kiri *Menike* simply. "And she will be of no trouble for she is but sixteen years of age."

' "We will see." I did not wish her to see that I would give in too easily. But I was flattered when she said that the girl would come if I spoke to her.

'I knew that this would have to be a matter of stealth. If I went to the girl's guardians I would have to spend money. And what was the use in wasting money on a young orphan girl? So little did my Suduhamy mean to me then that I was not willing to lose even a little money over her. But then how was I to know that a strange orphan girl would come to mean so much to me?

'Little by little I got all the information out from Kiri *Menike*. Then I planned the whole plot carefully as I would plan a piece of furniture in the *vadu maduva*.

'The girl's guardians were an old couple who had been burdened with the child after its mother died years ago. The mother had been a beautiful woman, like my Suduhamy, to whom the admiration of men was as necessary as the food she ate. The father, in a fit of jealousy, had taken a knife and cut her down. Of such a beginning came my Suduhamy. Fool that I was not to have realized that what begins in violence always ends in violence.

'The house in which she stayed with her guardians was small and poor and ill-protected at night. Kiri *Menike* told me that the old guardians were sound sleepers as well as being slightly deaf. My Suduhamy did not sleep with them. She had been given the little lean-to where she cooked all the meals. It would be an easy matter to get to her in the night.

'So one night when the moon was bright, I set off on my bicycle for Suduhamy's hut. I had brought with me a little clay lamp with a bottle of oil and a wick to light it. My blood was racing with excitement and I was enjoying every minute of the adventure. Never have I stolen a woman this way!

'When I reached the hut I dismounted and waited in the shadow of the *pila**, listening to the loud snoring of the old pair.

---

* veranda at the back

Those two snored together and the sound was like a waterfall thundering down a hillside. I lit the lamp and softly pushed open the rickety old door which groaned and moaned as if being pushed beyond its strength. But the old couple snored on undisturbed and it was an easy matter to step past them and go into the low smoke-blackened lean-to. It was as simple as that, this first meeting with my Suduhamy. I went into the lean-to and there she was. She lay on the mat sleeping like a child, her dark thick hair loose and framing her tiny round face.'

Diyonis *Baas* stopped as if he could go on no longer. His fierce old eyes filled with tears.

'*Aiyo*, how shall I describe her to you? My Suduhamy cannot be described with mere words alone. Even now I cannot remember how beautiful she looked. Perhaps it was the pure innocence in her face, so clean and untouched by any emotion, or perhaps the small perfect breasts as they rose and fell as she breathed under the loose jacket. Or was it the soft rounded limbs of this child-woman that caught at my heart-strings and held them forever in bondage?

'My heart beating strangely, I leant over her and let the light from the oil lamp fall on her face.

'She opened her eyes and looked straight at me without fear or any emotion. My heart flew into my mouth and the words that came out were as unsteady as a boat upon a rough sea. I had meant to broach the subject of her coming with me gently, tactfully, but now it gushed out like a water spout.

' "Do not be afraid," I said hastily. "I know your situation and I have come to take you. I shall try to look after you as kindly as I know how."

'She said nothing but lay there gazing up at me with those deep black eyes of hers.

' "Come, child, come," I tried to speak firmly but my voice betrayed my nervousness. "Do not be afraid. I will look after you better than those two snoring in there. I will truly be your kinsman."

'Then she got up, still without a word, and put up her hair into a *konde** as big as her head and buttoned the little jacket that had been so delightfully undone.

'I held up the lamp and she followed me meekly, still without

---

* a knot

a word, past the sleeping pair and out into the night. I placed her on the carrier of my bicycle and together we rode home. She did not utter a word on that trip and I had no need for words either. My thoughts were strong enough to hold us both together forever.

'And it was from that moment onwards that life changed its steady course. At first Kiri *Menike* was delighted to find Suduhamy in the house. She fell on her neck and wept as if she had found a long lost daughter. And Bissohamy, after she came back from looking after her husband, did her best to welcome Suduhamy though I could see that she was not a little surprised at what I had done. As for myself, I felt like a man who had reached the top of Sri Pada* after a long and weary climb.

'Many months went by and the feeling between Suduhamy and myself grew into a consuming passion. I found myself thinking of her every minute of the day and though she would be there each night waiting for me, it was never enough. I tell you, Leon Singho, it was like this almost to the very end. Never did our love come down to a comfortable feeling as it had become with Bissohamy. Suduhamy was like drink in my blood. The more I drank of her the more I wanted. The thirst was never satisfied enough to become boring.

'She never spoke much, Suduhamy, but all she wanted to say she said through those eyes of hers. She always remained remote and innocent and I could never find out her true feelings. Bissohamy always said that Suduhamy frightened her because she did not look human. But Bissohamy, I believe, was beginning to feel jealous. I had forbidden my Suduhamy to light the fire because the heat would burn her pure white skin and make her black. Bissohamy was angry and muttered something about how once upon a time I had preferred only what was black. But the real trouble began when she slipped on a piece of soap and hurt her leg.

'Bissohamy's leg swelled up to the full roundness of a jak fruit and had to be treated with oils by the *vederala***.

' "This has been done on purpose." Bissohamy eyes glittered through the pain. "And I know the person who did it too. She

---

*Adam's Peak, a sacred mountain; ** native doctor

must be sorry that I did not fall into the well and drown. She should have placed the soap a little closer to the well if she wanted to make sure of my death."

'Kiri *Menike*'s eyes opened wide in distress. "*Aiyo, aiyo* , do not speak this way. Why do you try to start trouble when we are so happy? Can we not live together peaceably?"

' "Nevertheless what I say is true. Though these days people never listen to what I say, it is still the truth." Bissohamy's eyes filled with tears and she looked away from me in hurt silence.

'Suduhamy came into the room then, and though her eyes smouldered as if she was hurt by what Bissohamy had said, she did not speak a word. Instead she sat down in her silent way and began to scrape a coconut for the evening meal. I went out of the *vadu maduva* for women's quarrels were not for me!

'But nevertheless I began to feel uneasy. If my three women began to fight, my life would be terrible. What man could live in the midst of women quarrelling? Though I had very little to do now with either Bissohamy or Kiri *Menike*, I did not want to lose them. Kiri *Menike* was still useful in the house and there was the child to whom I had grown attached. And Bissohamy was like a broken limb. Though serving no purpose she was still part of me and losing her would never be easy. Besides it was Bissohamy who had brought me luck in the beginning. And in a strange way I felt that if she went, my luck too would go with her.

'I never believed that my Suduhamy would bring me trouble. *Aiyo*, how could she? Such a child, so innocent and lovely. No, no, my Suduhamy could only bring joy and happiness. But I must watch out for her. See that the other two did not worry her with jealous talk. What would a tender young girl know of the feelings of older women? She was like a fly caught in a spider's web and I must look after her.

'With all this trouble in the house my mind wandered and I began to slacken in my work. Davith *Baas* complained that business was getting poor because. I was making too many mistakes in my work. But I no longer cared about the *vadu maduva*. I was too wrapped up in my Suduhamy! And when Kiri *Menike* died the following week, matters between Davith *Baas* and myself became worse.

'All I can now say is that I saw no reason then for Kiri *Menike*'s death. True she had been ailing for sometime, but then after the coming of Suduhamy she had recovered and had even helped in the cooking and the cleaning. My poor pale Kiri *Menike*! One moment she was there, gentle and kind to everybody alike, and then she was gone. I remember the night before she died she had complained of a pain in her stomach. So perhaps her old trouble had come back again to kill her.

'My Suduhamy worked hard and did everything for the funeral of my Kiri *Menike*. She washed the body and dressed it in a white saree, weeping bitterly all the while. And when Bissohamy sat like a stone and spoke no word to her, she did not seem to mind.

'A month later Davith *Baas* and I broke up the *vadu maduva* and he left for another village. I still remember the words he left me with because they sounded so strange then to my ears.

' "Look after Bissohamy," he said. "It is not easy to find women like her."

'I did not understand what he meant. Why should I look after Bissohamy who was quite capable of looking after herself? Besides, she was not ill or anything like that. Then I thought: "Had Bissohamy anything to do with Davith *Baas*?"

'If they had been meeting in secret I would surely kill her. I am a jealous man and would never share any of my women with another man. True Bissohamy had a husband, but then having a husband for whom she cared nothing was one thing, and meeting a lover in secret was quite a different matter. For a day or two I was blinded with rage. I took my bicycle and rode furiously up and down the road, looking like a madman. Then my temper cooled and reason returned. Bissohamy was not a woman to do anything in secret. If she had gone to Davith *Baas* she would have walked out on me first before doing so. She would have told me the truth.

'Nevertheless, I could not wholly bury the ugly suspicion. And, when three months later she too died of a stomach pain like Kiri *Menike*'s, my suspicious mind blinded me again to the truth.

'After I had buried my Bissohamy life was never the same, as I believed she had taken all my luck with her. Soon there was hardly anything to eat in the house and no money to buy food.

'Suduhamy began to complain for the first time since she came to my house. "The child cries with hunger and I can do nothing. *Aiyo*, even at my old guardians' house there was more to eat than here."

' "I will get rice, do not fear my *menike*," I consoled her. "Everybody in the village owes Diyonis *Baas* a little something and we will manage till I start work again."

'But she was never the same after that. She ill-treated the poor child till I took him away and gave him to a friend of mine to keep for a while. After the child went away it was a little better. Suduhamy complained less, but she took to deep fits of silent brooding when she would retire to a corner and sit for hours staring into space. From this trance she would wake up occasionally to accuse me of not caring for her any more. This was not true and I gave proof of this at night when I took her into my arms. But still she would accuse me of neglecting her.

'Then one night she confessed that she was with child. I do not know what other men feel when their women conceive, but as for me it was the greatest happiness I had yet enjoyed. My Suduhamy, my most precious of all jewels, was carrying my child and I was dazed with the mere thought of it. A out last our love was bearing fruit.

'I waited on her hand and foot. Never once did I permit her to pound the rice nor sweep the compound. The other women in the village laughed and told me it was good for Suduhamy to pound the rice.

' "It will make it easier for her to bear the child," they insisted.

'But I was stubborn. Suduhamy sat in the house and waited like a queen while I even cooked all our meals.

'I told her that we must now legalize our marriage so that she would become my true wife. This is the proof of my fondness for her, Leon Singho. To no other woman have I offered the position of my true wife.

'I tried to set up a little *vadu maduva* near the house. With the coming of the child I would have to start work again. But my mind was constantly hovering over Suduhamy and I could not think of other things. I cleared the space for a *vadu maduva* but did nothing further. The mere thought of work was a burden I wished to put off for a little while longer.

'Thus absorbed in each other and the coming child, my Suduhamy and I were pathetically unaware of the storm brewing in the village against us. Suduhamy rarely stepped out of the house now and though I went out for an occasional chew of betel or to borrow some rice, I swear to this day that I never saw any black looks or muttered threats among the men who stood in knots here and there on the road while I went by.

'Therefore, it hit me like a lightning bolt out of the sky. One day I was out in the jungle searching for a special kind of yam that my Suduhamy had got a craving to eat. It was not easy to find this yam, for it grew on a creeper and there are many different creepers growing on trees in the jungle. Then I saw a handful of men coming towards me and the leader among them was Appuhamy, the *sillara kade mudalali,* Bissohamy's husband. I greeted him pleasantly.

' *"Ayubowan*,* I am looking for a yam for my Suduhamy," I said.

'Appuhamy neither smiled nor answered back in greeting. His face turned grave and he kept looking at me as if he was seeing me for the first time.

' "What do you want, *aiya*?" I asked quickly. Suddenly I felt there was something wrong here.

' "We want to talk with you," he said shortly.

' "About what?" I asked in surprise, "and if it's talk you want, I am here, waiting. Though I warn you I cannot waste too much time because I must find this yam for my Suduhamy. You know how it is with women in that condition."

'At the very mention of my Suduhamy a change came over the men. They began to mutter and there were sullen looks passed from one to another.

' "We wish to talk with you," Appuhamy repeated loudly. "And we do not want to sit and listen to your talk about that low creature you call your wife!"

'I sprang up with a hoarse cry and went for his throat like a maddened dog. His throat came into my hands easily and I squeezed with all my might. There was a red haze in front of my eyes and a roaring sound in my ears. My foot slipped and I fell to the ground, dragging his weight on to me.

'I felt hands separating us and then I was dragged to my feet and held in an iron grip. Appuhamy's face, filled with hate, towered before me for he was a big man.

' "You low country dog!" he screamed contemptuously, "you come into our village and not content with taking our women

---

* Greetings

from us, you must kill them too! *Aiyo, aiyo*, my poor Bissohamy! What she must have endured at your hands! And in the end to have died at that woman's hands!"

'The blood pounded in my ears. I gazed back at Appuhamy, a long smouldering steady gaze.

' "Careful of those words you utter, *aiya*. I am not a man to be insulted and pushed aside easily. And what is this talk about killing Bissohamy?" I asked slowly.

'But before he could speak another man thrust his words between us.

' "We say that your precious Suduhamy killed Bissohamy and Kiri *Menike*. Your Suduhamy, who is as cruel and underhanded as a devil. She poisoned the other two woman. How else could both have died so suddenly and with a severe pain in the stomach too?"

' "Lies, all lies, and may the gods strike you dead for it!" I yelled. "Yes, let lightning strike you dead for uttering such lies! My Suduhamy cannot even poison an ant. She who is kind and gentle and timid like the deer that roams in the jungle."

' "She is not timid and gentle like the deer. She is cunning and deep like *Kuveni* the she-devil," retorted Appuhamy. "I can cry now when I think of how my poor Bissohamy used to complain about her. But you never listened to Bissohamy, did you? After taking all that she had to offer, you only listened to that foul creature you shamelessly call your wife. *Aiyo*, it is useless to speak to ears that are deaf to a devil's faults! It is folly to think so highly of any woman. It is asking for trouble."

' "My Suduhamy cannot kill," I kept on repeating stubbornly.

' "This has become a matter for the police. If you do not talk we will go to the police."

' "*Aiyo*, how can a child like Suduhamy kill? Do not speak of my Suduhamy this way I beg you. She is a good girl and people are jealous of her. That is why they say such things about her."

'But they went on saying that she had killed. And suddenly I was afraid for my Suduhamy's life. I kept her away from all this talk, yet she must have known for she stopped going down even to the well to get water.

'Then one night, that last night of our lives together—only I did not know it then—my Suduhamy came to me and looking down with tears in her eyes, she said, "Everybody is angry with me. Even you, I can feel the change in you too. I am but a poor motherless girl and it is better that I end my life and the child's tonight."

'I could not speak for my throat felt too full.

' "Why should I have harmed those two who did nothing to me! You were my life and I lived only for you. I never even spoke much to those two," she said in an unhappy voice.

'I took her then into my arms and cradled her to sleep. I still could find no words to comfort her. But I think she was comforted by my arms close around her, for she soon fell asleep.

'But I could not sleep for a long time. I lay there on the mat with my eyes wide open and stared at the thatched roof, my mouth dry with fear. As far as I could see there seemed to be no solution unless I took my Suduhamy and moved into another village. But it was too late to make plans to escape. For even as I lay there in fear and misery, sleep stole over me like a thief and took away my Suduhamy. When I woke up in the morning my Suduhamy was dead.

'She had hanged herself from the tree in our compound and her body was cold to my embrace. When the men came to take her to the police station only I was there, sitting like a statue beneath the tree from which my Suduhamy hung.'

Leon Singho looked respectfully at the little old man who had lived through so much. If Leon Singho lived even half of it he would consider his life well spent.

Diyonis *Baas'* tale was finished and now he lay spent and weary as if he had finished a long and painful task. His eyes were closed but on his face was a look of satisfaction, of peace. It was as if he had achieved, successfully, what he had set out to achieve.

He stirred and sighed deeply. Then opened his eyes and looked at Leon Singho.

'Talking about my Suduhamy has eased the pain I had here,' he said and patted his chest.

'Yes, it was like bringing out all the poison that was inside. Now I am cleansed and free.'

'Did they find out the truth in the end, *aiya*? Did Suduhamy kill Bissohamy and Kiri *Menike*?' asked Leon Singho.

Diyonis *Baas* winced and the pain returned to his eyes again.

'Do not speak of this again, I beg of you. It only confuses me again and brings back the pain of remembering Suduhamy. Who can know the strange ways of women? And especially of a woman like my Suduhamy? I had to run from that village myself because the police came and said that it was I who had killed Kiri *Menike*; also Bissohamy and my Suduhamy when I had tired of them each in turn. They said that I had done this thing and then very cleverly had made it look like my Suduhamy had done it in a fit of jealous rage. They had proof, they said, proof that I had killed all three myself.

'Perhaps it would be better to take the blame on myself and spare my Suduhamy. I will do anything for her. I do not like to think of her as being jealous or mad even, though she would sit for hours just silently brooding. Perhaps, women, when they carry children in their womb, become strangely jealous and suspicious of other women. I had thought my Suduhamy to be a rare and precious jewel. Perhaps I was mistaken.

'My Suduhamy could never willingly commit a bad deed. She killed because of her love for me. She loved me so deeply that she could not bear to see the other two come between us. The police *ralahamy** said that I had purposely fallen asleep so that Suduhamy would kill herself. Knowing that she wanted to die that night I should have kept awake, he said.

'I tell you, Leon Singho, now that you know of my love for her, do you think I would have let my Suduhamy die? *Aiyo*, my Suduhamy! Among all the women that came after her, never did I find a woman like that again!'

---

* officer

Suvimalee Karunaratne

The Golden Oriole

When Miss Vitharne walked into the classroom that morning, like the other mornings during that month, it was apparent to all that something strange and wonderful had happened in her life. It was in the way she carried herself—as if she had been elevated suddenly to a unique position of dignity. She seemed afire too, like a small sun bestowing a scintillating radiance around and about her.

'I want you to know,' she told the girls in a low authoritative voice so different from the shrill tone she normally used, 'that love is a very special magical sort of thing. I wish each and every one of you may experience it one day.' Having made this enigmatic statement she beamed on them like one who had been favoured by a particularly bountiful goddess and was magnanimously invoking the same good fortune upon them. She was more than content to see the young upturned faces register surprise, and when a few giggled and exchanged covert remarks behind handkerchiefs she beamed still more. Miss Vitharne obviously was above such petty inconsequentials that day. She turned and busied herself with writing complex and compound sentences on the blackboard for analysis.

That the girls showed surprise at Miss Vitharne's remark was not a wonder for it was not the type of remark one would expect her to make. Everyone knew Miss Vitharne to be studious and timorous, motivated to a great extent by religious impulses. It was well known that she spent her free time poring over Buddhist scriptures, participating in temple rituals and going on pilgrimages with her mother. She had even taken part in one or two Buddhist symposiums on the radio and these had been major occasions in her life.

The students began to copy down the sentences in their exercise books and silently worked them out. Having finished writing, Miss Vitharne went up to the window and for a short space of time lost herself freely and sensuously in the verdant greenery of flapping banana leaves, coconut palms and the hibiscus hedge. A bird swooped down from a shady tamarind tree, spreading out brilliant yellow wings. It flew low over the grass and then up and away into the sky. Miss Vitharne watched, fascinated. It was not every day one saw a golden oriole—which the Sinhalese called a yellow-robed thief. With such splendidly hued wings it must certainly be a bird of good omen, she thought, for yellow was an auspicious colour. It was the colour of gold, of ripe grain, of sunshine. It was also the colour of the robes worn by Buddhist monks; but that was rather odd, she pondered. Why had such a stoically celibate clergy chosen yellow for their robes? Yellow had so many connotations of fertility, of ripeness, of material fulfilment. Perhaps that was why the hermit monks who shunned society and meditated in the solitude of forests preferred robes of the browner, russet hue. . . .

'Miss Vitharne.' A gentle voice nudged the rushing stream of her thoughts, but she did not hear it. 'Miss Vitharne,' the voice called louder, cutting through her consciousness, startling her.

'Yes, what is it, Ranjini?' She recognized the young typist from the school office standing by her.

'There's a telephone call for you.'

'Thank you.'

Miss Vitharne glided blithely out of the room, not unlike the golden oriole that had taken wing to the sky a little while ago. She felt her spirits soar exhilaratingly. No doubt that would be Aunt Beatrice calling her again. She must really put a stop to these constant summons on the phone. Not that Miss Vitharne was irritated by them, but Aunt Beatrice must not be made to feel that she was at her beck and call any time of the day, especially during her lessons. True, Aunt Beatrice had made a match for her, but she must not, on the strength of that, take advantage of her. Yes, she must put a stop to these phone calls once and for all.

About a month ago Aunt Beatrice had actually brought Miss Vitharne a proposal of marriage. It had caused a pleasant excitement in her but her mother had viewed it with singular disinterest and even suspicion. Of course Aunt Beatrice herself was quite above any kind of suspicion. The worst anyone could say of her was that she was a confirmed busybody. That was one thing Aunt Beatrice believed in staunchly—being a busybody in the interest of other people's welfare. Especially in making matches for her innumerable nieces and nephews. The field offered her ample scope for her energetic talents.

Her mother's suspicions were based on her experience of masculine temperament.

'Does he know Rupa's age?' her mother had inquired of Aunt Beatrice bluntly. Miss Vitharne had flinched. Delicacy was not one of her mother's strong points.

Aunt Beatrice looked a little baffled. 'What for telling Rupa's age? I tell you, child, all that is not so important. He is not looking for somebody very pretty or young or anything like that. It seems his wife died about a year ago. She must have been about Rupa's age. What he wants now is a nice good girl who will look after him and do everything nicely in the home.'

'Does he know that there is no dowry?'

'Don't worry about all that, child. After all, Rupa has got a B.A. degree, no? That is quite enough for him. He is a very simple, good man.'

'And children?'

'He has got several already, so he won't be wanting any more.'

Her mother frowned. 'Rupa has been quite content to live as she has been living,' she said shortly. 'She is always busy with her school work and her religious activities.'

'But surely, are you trying to tell me that all these things are better than getting married.'

'The point is Rupa is quite happy as she is. Everything depends on one's attitude and Rupa seems to find happy fulfilment in the things she does.'

Miss Vitharne had been surprised at her mother's words and her absolute disinterest in the proposal. She darted a quick look of angry resentment at her. Why did her mother take it upon herself to decide matters—especially matters that affected her life so profoundly? Surely she was assuming the role of Fate in her life?

'You don't mind, no, if I ask Rupa herself?' Aunt Beatrice asked, almost as if she were able to read Miss Vitharne's thoughts.

For a moment she experienced a mixed sensation of confusion and embarrassment. How could she openly exhibit a liking for the proposal? It would not become her mature years. So she cleared her throat nervously and said primly, 'I am quite happy as I am as Mother just told you. The question of marriage has never bothered me all these years.'

'Then you don't want me to pursue this matter further?'

There was a pause during which time Miss Vitharne's heart sank a little.

'There is no point in pursuing things that are not destined to take place,' her mother said after a short pause. 'One should accept one's karma—fate—as it comes.'

Miss Vitharne was again irritated by her mother's decisive tone of voice. How was she so sure that she was not destined to marry? True she was not a young girl any more, but then neither was the man who was being proposed a budding youth himself.

Perhaps Aunt Beatrice had felt instinctively how she felt. That was probably why she had telephoned her at school on the following day. Miss Vitharne did not have a telephone in her dingy little row house on the outskirts of the city, and her gratitude knew no bounds when Aunt Beatrice telephoned.

'Rupa, now without getting angry, tell me, child, do you like this thing or no?' Aunt Beatrice asked. 'He says he would like very much to meet you. Shall I bring him to your place?'

These words had caused an excited flurry in the region of her heart, but she had only said, 'I really don't know what Mother will say.'

'Never mind what she will say,' Aunt Beatrice said impatiently. 'The trouble with your mother is that she is too proud.'

So that evening itself Aunt Beatrice had brought him to their home. Miss Vitharne had expected to see an older-looking man, but all the same he looked kind. Throughout the visit he kept casting glances in her direction which made her ears burn. After some time she felt herself welcoming these glances, which had the effect of diffusing her whole being with a warm tingling sensation which she had thought not possible for her to feel any more. Once when he looked at her she boldly lifted her eyelids and even fluttered their lashes a little. But this she regretted immediately, sensing the mild astonishment it caused. His eyes rested on her face inquiringly and it became difficult for her to hide her distress.

Her mother was far from pleased by the visit but Miss Vitharne was too full of pulsating hopes and dizzy exhilaration to feel her displeasure. The next day Aunt Beatrice—how truly kind and considerate she was—phoned and gave the good news. He was keen, it seemed, and had expressed a wish to visit her again. Naturally, she agreed happily, and so it was that he began to visit her every evening, like a prayer. Each day Miss Vitharne became gayer and bolder. Her hair, which she had been accustomed to tie in a severe knot at the back of her head gave way to a loose informal plait, and sometimes even remained unbound, brazening luxuriant tresses to his admiring gaze. Her body felt charged with a new motivation. She could almost feel the surge of sap.

'See how one's karma works,' her mother remarked one day. 'Just think how long you had to wait to meet the correct man.' These were her mother's first words of encouragement—her unofficial blessings. Miss Vitharne, who was combing out her hair in front of the mirror, thought to herself that she might well have missed her chance on account of her mother, but at that moment her eyes took in her reflection and it fairly knocked the breath and also the resentment out of her. She could but marvel at her own transformation—her eyes looking luminously bright and her skin, which had been rather dry and showing signs of coarse maturity, now gave an appearance of delicate softness. It was as if the burgeoning happiness within her, like a water lily opening out in the morning sunshine, was reflecting itself in her face. 'What a brittle thing our personality is,' she contemplated in a brief moment of self-knowledge, 'dependent on so many external and internal factors, we change from moment to moment. They say matter remains static only for seventeen thought-moments.' But strangely enough this fleeting insight didn't bring with it any equanimity. Rather, she felt holier for having thought it. Soon she was sallying forth to school like a boat with sails unfurled and billowing ecstatically.

At school they had begun to notice the curious change in her too. In the staff room they were quick to catch the meanings hinted at by her oblique remarks.

'One has to experience love to know what it is,' she announced stretching herself out lazily on a chair with a half-smile on her lips.

'Aha!' they laughed, 'so our friend here has found herself someone at last.'

'Who is the lucky man?' another cried.

'What lucky man?' she wanted to know, pretending to frown.

'Congratulations, you dark horse, when is the wedding?'

'I really don't know what you all are talking about,' she said, showing a becoming embarrassment and escaping from the barrage of questions she herself had brought down on her ears. But amidst all this teasing hilarity she was aware of a few resentful glances. Well, they would be even more resentful when they see the ring. The day before he had been asking her what kind of ring she would like to wear. If they only knew from what a well-to-do family he was and what a responsible government post he held—how jealous they would be! It was difficult for her to hold in all this elation. All she could do was to make oblique remarks and look as enigmatic as she could.

So now as she hurried out of class and walked across the bit of garden space towards the office block, she was conscious of all eyes following her. She wondered what Aunt Beatrice had to say. Most probably it was something not very important. She had been threatening to invite them all to her house for a party in their honour. Maybe she wanted to fix the date. Well anyway, she must put a stop to these interruptions, once and for all.

Miss Vitharne ran up the few steps to the office, scattered her radiant smiles among the office girls and took up the receiver with aplomb.

'Hello, yes?'

'Rupa, Aunt Beatrice speaking here. . . .'

'Yes, Aunt Beatrice, do say what you have to say quickly. I was right in the middle of a class. The principal doesn't like our work interrupted every now and again, you know.'

A short pause followed this somewhat crisply delivered speech. The silence almost crackled.

'I'm very sorry, child. I really don't know how to tell you what I have to tell you. . . .'

Miss Vitharne experienced a sharp sensation of alarm. Aunt Beatrice's tone conveyed something drastically wrong.

'He. . . he says. . . it seems he can't make up his mind. . . just yet. You see. . . hello, Rupa? Are you there?'

Miss Vitharne drew in her breath heavily and managed to make a stifled noise in her throat. The whole world seemed to have stopped dead. A roar of rushing blood seemed to crash and pound about her ears.

'You know. . . the thing is he can't get over his wife's death it seems. Poor man. I feel sorry for him also. Some people are very temperamental, you know.'

The silence yawned between them across the wire. She felt it attempting to probe her mind.

'I'm very sorry about it,' Aunt Beatrice ventured, 'but Rupa you mustn't go and let this upset you now.'

'It's all right,' Miss Vitharne said mechanically, resisting the urge to slam down the receiver.

'What's to be done, child? These things happen. As your mother said—what a wise person she is—one cannot force karma to make things happen that are not destined to happen. You must take these ups and downs as they come. I am truly sorry it turned out this way. Wish you all the luck in the world.'

Miss Vitharne forced out a polite 'thank you' and dropped the receiver. She began to walk back slowly, her legs dragging. She strove to control her facial muscles and resolved to remain poised and calm however difficult the feat. Two veins swelled on either side of her neck with the effort. She re-entered the classroom and resumed her stance in front of the window. The trees and bushes were a green blur among which her eyes darted hither and thither like angry gnats. She could not feel herself a part of it. The world around her could draw no sympathetic response from her.

The stark blue sky into which the golden oriole had disappeared was empty now but a movement nearer her obtruded on her line of vision. Two brown mynahs with yellow beaks and yellow legs were busily pecking at the ground. Miss Vitharne watched them going through the motions of their companionable endeavour to ferret out food. Suddenly tears sprang into her eyes. The pulsing, quivering, pregnant life outside, impinging on her senses, was too much for her and she began to cry.

James Goonewardene

The Doughty Men of Purantota

The people of Purantota were not pleased about the bridge they were going to build, as it was on the doorstep of their village. It was to come up barely a quarter of a mile away from the *kadamandiya*.* The encroachment was going to bring an end to their independence. They did not know how, but the idea had been put into their heads, by someone—they did not know who—and it had begun to worry them. The surveyors had come with their instruments several weeks earlier. They were followed by others who stood officiously on the bank of the river and held conferences. The movement of vehicles came almost on their heels. They brought men and building materials, and they continued to flow up and down for a while afterwards. Then came the drum beaters, announcing to the villagers that they were needed to help build the bridge. The villagers watched it all from a distance as suspiciously as a herd of deer that had scattered at the approach of an animal it feared.

Eventually, as they regained their confidence, they ventured to emerge from hiding, and registered as labourers, woodcutters and builders. For a week then, they worked on the bridge-site as hired hands. They cut down the trees, pushed over the boulders and turned up the soil. Then, stage by stage, they advanced, clearing the way for the bridge. There was all this work to do, and they were doing it without really knowing why. Certainly the money they offered at the bridge-site was good. It took away one type of freedom and gave them another—gave them 'money freedom'. They suddenly found they could buy things they couldn't afford before. It was exciting—this new freedom. But this was all for a short time.

---

* market-place

One hot morning they dropped their axes and took off to the shelter of the trees still left standing. These trees were part of an old jungle they had known for a longer time than they could remember. The jungle and its trees had been part of the village's history. As boys they had played among the trees on their way to school, or had sat in their shade, while waiting for the ferry-boat to come across the river. They knew the river; knew its moods, and both loved and feared it. These trees and the river they had always thought of as being part of their village's inheritance. They had to protect them, also their right and access to them. They had to keep them safe for themselves and their children.

There was only the thud of a single axe now. Someone was still chopping a tree down to the left. On the right the axes had been silenced. Then the last axe stopped echoing. Andoris Rala turned his head to look round him. There was just himself now, alone by the kumbuk tree. Brampi too, his friend, had left him. He too had gone to take shelter. Andoris Rala began to move away then, slowly, as if he had a great distance to go, and there was all the time in which to do it. There were suddenly many things to think about but there was no time to do them in. There was only the seeing now, and there was the doing. The men were seated there, squatting on the grass like men come to trade at the *poya* fair, chewing betel, smoking *beedis* and gossiping.

Girigoris was the one he feared, the one whose thinking was kept hidden like a dagger in a sheath. He alone had this puckered face as if there was a night in his brain into which light was never admitted. The others had un-puckered open faces in which no mystery had yet been written. Armanis, the brick-maker, Arnolis, the cowherd, Ekmon, the blacksmith's assistant, and a couple of others, and finally Davith Singho, the loafer, and of course, Girigoris. Davith Singho was seated with his back against a tree, smoking a *beedi* as if all this was part of a routine—work, sleep, rest, and then work again, with a little pleasure thrown in for good measure, or just loafing maybe, when there was nothing else to do.

'If we stop to pant after every stroke of the axe, when will we finish this job?' asked Andoris Rala. 'There's still an hour before the midday break.'

'Even a bull stops work when it's tired, don't you know?' replied Davith Singho.

'The man who works the least gets tired the quickest,' said Andoris Rala.

'Huh, such foolish talk. You would think, hearing him talk, that we sit on our behinds and play with ourselves,' snapped back Davith Singho.

Davith Singho, a young man of about thirty, everyone knew, was notoriously lazy. He had drifted away from the village. From time to time he would work in the dock, in the city. When he was out of work he would drift back.

'That, no doubt, you learned in the city,' retorted Andoris Rala. 'You sit so long in one place it is a wonder grass doesn't grow between your toes. You should know what you do with yourself in that time.'

The men laughed.

'What else can he do as a part-time labourer other than sit on his behind and play with himself?' said Sarnelis.

'That's what comes from looking for easy money,' said another.

Davith Singho drew out his *beedi* and spat noisily. 'I left the mud so that you buffaloes can wallow in it.'

'You leave the mud to us and go playing with yourself in the city,' said Sarnelis, 'the trade they taught you out there.'

'Buffaloes will always be buffaloes. So buffalo talk is all you'll hear from this bunch. Sometime I'll tell you about the city.' Davith Singho rose to his feet, kicked a mug lying in his path and stalked off. They let him go.

'We do wrong to tease him,' said Andoris Rala, feeling mortified suddenly. 'It was my mistake. When times are not propitious even the *labu* fruit is bitter.'

Girigoris cleared his throat pointedly and continued to prepare his chew of betel. 'These, indeed, are unpropitious times but not for the reasons Andoris Rala gives,' he said.

'For what reason, then, are they unpropitious?'

'For reasons that only the gods know,' replied Girigoris.

'Sometimes people speaking in their own tongues say it is the voice of the gods.'

'It has to be an unpropitious time that strangers should climb over our stiles as if the whole village was now a public highway.'

'Mhm, mhm, *attha, attha**,' grunted Heen Banda, Girigoris'

---

* true

friend, affirmatively.

'This bridge when it comes up will be the thing that will destroy us,' said Girigoris, encouraged by Heen Banda's support. 'It will be the point of the knife held at our throats.'

'How will this be so?' asked Arnolis.

'Because then there will no longer be a village here. The bridge will belong to no one. So will the village be no one's.'

The men were suddenly staring at Girigoris.

'How will it belong to no one? We will cross the bridge like anyone else, and faster than the ferry-boat.'

Girigoris smiled—a man of unusual appearance, he had his head placed directly on his shoulders as if a neck had never been necessary.

It was thrust forward in a way that was not unlike that of an anthropoid. He even walked with a slouch.

'Is that all you can think about? Can't you see that the bridge will stand out there like an evil spirit whom no one can tame? The buses and other man-made machines will be constantly over it. We will be the dirt on the roadside. New fangled things will creep into the village. Strangers will order us about.'

The others rose and drew nearer, the better to hear the debate.

'That's right. What our brother says is true,' said Heen Banda, 'it will belong to the buses and lorries. We will be the rubbish on the wayside.'

'This is foolish talk. To say we cannot tame it is foolish talk,' said Arnolis. 'If a man builds, he can destroy what he builds.'

'Look, my friend, to destroy is not to tame a thing. To destroy it is to finish it. To tame is to control it. Look how we control our paddy. We irrigate the land. We watch the first leaf sprout. We transplant it. Then we harvest it. A bridge, what is it but a thing of stone and steel—a thing without life. It will push us out of the way. Like the *ahikuntakayo** we will bundle up our things and depart. Other machines will follow the bridge. Those who remain here will be like machines. Look at Davith Singho. He is no longer one of us. He has become a bit of rubbish come from the docks.'

Davith Singho, who had just come back from his stroll, sprang into life on hearing himself spoken of thus.

'You pack of earth despoilers, what makes you talk of me all

---

* gypsies

the time? Do you now invite me to rape your mothers to prove I am of the same breed as you wretches?'

'Come, come now,' admonished Brampi. 'We quarrel here like bazaar curs. To trouble our heads about things not yet taken place is like the man who prepares to bathe while he is still seven leagues from the river. We villagers have one great virtue. We are talkers. We talk till the earth splits apart.'

'That is wisely said,' said Arnolis. 'We, indeed, do nothing but talk. We are like the *kirala*. The foolish bird lies on its back and sticks its feet up for fear the sky will drop on his nest.'

Some weeks later Girigoris awoke one morning feeling an ache in his back. He was grateful it was not a day of work at the bridge-site. Since he commenced work here he had come to fear the return of the ache in his back. After his wife had left him he had occupied himself with helping the ageing monk in the conduct of the affairs of the temple. This had kept him busy; also his mind free from worry. The scandal created by the elopement of his wife with a toddy tapper from a village several miles away was still fresh in the minds of the people. He was still trying to live that down, but as chief lay custodian of the temple he had recently acquired a sense of security and a feeling of importance. The temple would be the means by which, in the end, he would wreak vengeance on his fate. Ill-luck had dogged his steps. Even his birth had been a misfortune, they said. He was told that his birth had so drained his mother of energy that for several weeks people didn't know if she would survive it. The temple was where one usually found him. When he was not in the temple he was accustomed to staying in his hut on the outskirts of the village. He stayed here like a recluse, nursing his grievances. One reached this hut by a devious footpath which wound round some abandoned land and across a scrub jungle. As the chief *dayakaya** of the temple he was kept busy. He had to organize the monk's *dana***, collect funds to pay the drummer, have an occasional *pinkama*[+], and attend to a variety of other details. The *devale*,[++] however, was the chief of his concerns. However hard-pressed the villagers were, they had to find the means to ward off misfortune that the astrologers predicted, and misfortune was not so rare an occurrence. There was a rumour that *devale* offerings found their way into Girigoris' pockets. No one had

---

* lay custodian; ** meals; [+] ceremony; [++] shrine

been able to prove this, but it was cómmon knowledge that this was so. But what did it matter, they thought, if indeed he interceded with the gods on their behalf and there were results.

Girigoris thus awoke this morning feeling this ache in his back. He felt miserable. He hadn't the desire even to go among the bushes to empty his bowels. It was lucky, he thought, that it should come on a *poya* day. He had, recently, come to fear this ache in his back. The thought of getting up now to set out to Heen Banda's depressed him, but it had to be done. He had to be fit enough to go to work. So he dragged himself out of bed and went slowly through the scrub jungle, along the winding footpath. Heen Banda wasn't at home. He had gone to the pond for a bath, his wife told him.

'I shall then wait for him,' said Girigoris. He lowered himself painfully on to the couch in the veranda. Podi *Menike* withdrew into the house and reappeared with the betel tray.

'A chew of betel—if you wish.'

She placed the tray on a stool and withdrew to stand in the doorway.

'Good,' said Girigoris. 'A chew of betel will perhaps do me good. I have not eaten a thing this morning.'

'*Apoi**, *mahattaya*. . . . why so?'

'It's this ache in my back. . . .'

'*Apoi*, not to eat in the morning. . . it is harmful. I shall get you something else then. . . a cup of tea, maybe?'

'Not a thing, not a thing. It is good to punish this old body of mine. We soften ourselves with too much comfort. It is good to starve the body sometimes.'

'My husband will blame me later for letting you starve. Let me get you some food.'

'Podi *Menike*, do you know me as a man who weakens about a thing like food. I chastise my body when it is necessary.'

'Don't I know it? Heen Banda talks of nothing but of your great strength of will.'

'Mhn!' grunted Girigoris. 'I don't deny that.'

He was pleased his reputation had spread. He lifted his eyes to take a better look at her. She was slightly built and flat-chested, and her arms skinny. He suddenly felt bitter and angry. Only the flat-chested ones will flatter me, he thought. The round,

---

* Alas

full-blooded ones will not give me even a glance, I am of little use to them. At the critical moment it always fails me, the wretched, ineffective bit of appendage. The ache suddenly returned, and he groaned. When he became aware of his deformities the ache was always bad.

'Mhn, where's this husband of yours? He takes so long over his bath. Maybe he'll be there all day.'

'*Apoi*, no *mahattaya*, he must be already on his way. An hour has passed since he left for his bath.'

'He'd better come soon. This ache gets worse every minute.' He took another look at Podi *Menike*. 'Some of these women are unfaithful to their men. I wonder if she will be unfaithful to Heen Banda if the situation arises.' Podi *Menike* smiled under his scrutiny. Then she looked up and saw her husband come along the path.

'There, he comes now,' she said.

'Mhn!' murmured Heen Banda. 'What fetches you to my door so early?' He paused a moment, a bucket in his hand and a towel slung over his arm. Girigoris merely glanced up at his friend; a man of few words, he avoided the usual pleasantries. Heen Banda scrutinized his friend's face.

'Not well, I see. . . your back as usual. Give me a moment while I put these things away.'

He returned a moment later and sat Girigoris down and began his examination, asking him about his present condition and how he had felt the previous day. He was actually rather pleased that Girigoris, the village cynic, should come to him for treatment. Girigoris did not really have faith in Heen Banda's remedies, but having no other person to go to, and his ailment not being serious, he had come along now to have a shot at the old *vedarala's* medicine.

'*Vathey**,*' intoned Heen Banda gravely. 'This is the old *vathey*. He'll have to try the old *kasaya* ** once more. It worked on the earlier occasion. It must do so again.'

'Mhn!' grunted Girigoris,' 'will it make me fit to go to work tomorrow?'

'To the bridge-site? Oh yes. You will be completely well by morning.'

---

* literally 'wind' (flatulence), but more frequently applied to rheumatism; **decoction

'Mhn!' moaned Girigoris.

After the remedy had been prescribed the two men relaxed awhile. Heen Banda picked up a chew of betel. When he had chewed it for several moments he squirted a red-coloured jet of betel juice through carefully shaped lips.

'Is this true you plan to have a special pooja at the *devale*?'

'Yes, this is true,' said Girigoris. 'We can't leave things to chance. The *devathavos* cared for the village in the past. We must care for them in return or they will withdraw their favour. The deities are like human beings. They get annoyed. Strangers have started to tramp over places that were sacred to them. It is no wonder that they now turn their faces against the village.'

'This is true. We forget what the ancients have so faithfully done to protect the village. We neglect these old practices.'

'I have heard that Andoris Rala has things to say about this pooja. Why should he be so concerned now? People have always offered pooja to the deities.'

'I have not heard that he opposes this.'

'Ah, he does not oppose it publicly, but he opposes it all the same. I do not like the way Andoris Rala goes after all these outsiders who tramp about here. We must not, however, worry ourselves too much about him. He is not really one of this village. He's a man from the south who has been settled here barely ten years. I believe I can count on your assistance, Heen Banda, if we ever need it.'

'You can count on me. It must not be said that I failed the village in its need.'

'I knew I could count on you, Heen Banda. We must see who else is a friend of the village. Well, I must go now. Ananda Joti *Hamuduruwo** may wonder why I do not turn up this morning. Tell him, if you meet him, that I have not been well. Maybe, if I feel better, I shall go there later in the day. I shall bring you something for the *kasaya*.'

'Don't concern yourself about such trivial things. You may offer a *pandura*** on my behalf at the *devale*, if you wish.'

'That I shall certainly do. It's an evil man who says he does not need his gods.'

'He certainly is.'

Girigoris brooded on what had to be done. Andoris Rala being

---

* priest; ** offering

put in charge of the labour pool at the bridge-site had been a setback for him. As a *dayakaya* of the temple the leadership in such matters should have been his. Andoris Rala would always be the great obstruction to his ambitions. Already he had become too big for his shoes. He must be checked, but how?

When Girigoris set his mind on some project he had the persistence and clinging quality of a limpet on a rock. He realized he needed help from outside the village. So he went looking for astrologers, weather prophets, dynamiters and others capable of helping him in his plans. The meeting was called one *poya* morning. They were to meet at Heen Banda's and everyone who had been asked had already arrived that morning barring Girigoris. The veranda being too narrow for the men, stools were placed in the yard, just outside. The betel tray had been passed around twice already and Girigoris had still not arrived. They chewed betel, smoked cigars, and waited. Finally, he came. He took the vacant chair and surveyed the rustic assembly like a general would inspect his troops.

'Mhn. I see everyone's here. Mhn, that's good,' he said.

He waved aside the betel tray.

'But this is not enough. We must get the others. We must get everyone to join us. This is a matter that should concern everyone in the village. If anyone can come here and do as he pleases—build bridges, pull down trees, cut roadways on grounds that have been sacred to the people of this village—there is no knowing how far they will go,' Girigoris paused. He had to tread cautiously. Andoris Rala was still popular in the village. Whatever he did had to be done with circumspection. Certainly, he had to be discredited, if not now at least later, but until then Girigoris had to proceed warily. He cast his eyes around at the assembled men. They were of different moulds and characters, but had one thing in common. They believed in the independence of their village, and whatever happened the village had to be protected from outside interference.

'I do not believe,' he continued, 'that there is anyone here who would like to see our village become a *palu* kanatte*** in which any stranger could come and plant his manioc and feed his cattle in. We have no other place to go to in any case, but more than that our fathers preserved it for us, and it is our duty

---

* deserted; ** cemetery

to preserve it for our children. I have no children of my own. I consider all children as mine. If a time comes when we, the older ones, cannot hold up our heads in dignity, what will become of our children? But remember, there are those who think differently from us. Not everyone is anxious to preserve the traditions of this village. There are people here, like Davith Singho, who will exchange the village for a bottle of *kasippu**. But I must say this for Davith Singho, that when he lost interest in the village he left it. He had come back, but only for a short time. He will leave it again. I am sure of that. If there are others like him it is only right that they too leave the village, leave it to us to protect it. We don't interfere with the affairs of other villages. It is what we expect of them, that they don't interfere with ours.'

'Yes, quite right,' echoed Heen Banda, 'if they don't care for the village that nourishes them it is right that they too go from it.'

'That's what I say,' said Girigoris. 'This village is ours. If it is necessary to destroy the bridge to preserve our independence we must do so.'

The men glanced at each other uneasily.

'It is this we must talk about now,' went on Girigoris. 'We must discover if we who have gathered here are ready to destroy the bridge if such a thing becomes necessary.'

The men glanced at each other again.

'But we all work there and help build this bridge,' protested Arnolis. 'I cannot understand why we should then want to destroy it.'

'Ah, this is true, I work on it myself, but to preserve our independence I am ready to destroy it. It is what we all must be prepared to do.'

'I agree that we must do everything possible to protect our village and its traditions, but we must seek to do it without resorting to violence,' said Arnolis.

Girigoris turned his eyes slowly on Arnolis, as if he were a wayward child who could not understand simple things.

'I do not say we must necessarily do this, but the readiness to do this is the test of how strongly we feel for our village. I think my friend here does not understand what we are trying to do here. *Ahimsa*** and *maithri*+ do not mean we must look on while

---

* illicit liquor; ** non-violence; + loving-kindness

our homes and children are swallowed up by the devil. The gods themselves have been pushed to anger. The rains on the hills have commenced earlier than they are accustomed to. This surely is a sign that the gods are moved to anger. The river has risen, and as surely as I stand here, it will rise further. I have talked with people who know. They are certain that a great calamity is about to befall the village from such rain and floods as we have not seen before. It will be the rains and the floods that will destroy the bridge. We might prevent such disaster by making peace with the gods, or surely these things will come to pass, and for our neglect we will be destroyed as well. Mark my words, the floods will flow over the fields, wash away the crop and hurl down the structures they have laid in the river. Will not this be a sign from the gods? What greater sign do you need?'

'But why will the gods be angry that strangers come to build a bridge here?' asked Arnolis. 'Surely bridges will come and roads expand.'

'Mhn, Arnolis asks many question. When will there be an end to his questions? For my part I know the people have turned their minds away from things they have always paid heed to. When did the people here last perform a *pinkama* at the temple? The coffers of the *devale* are empty. Is this not a sign that evil spirits have taken hold of the minds of the people? Our hearts have been turned away from the gods. We have planned to perform a cleansing ceremony at the *devale's* premises. I do not believe anyone is opposed to this. Those of us who still care for this village will partake of this ceremony. What more we must do will depend on what the gods want of us.'

Girigoris showed a capacity for rhetoric and speech-making that no one present there had suspected he had. They were silenced before it and had no counter arguments to offer.

'I see by your silence that you feel yourselves that the situation needs a drastic remedy.'

Girigoris had waited in silence all these years, nursing his numerous grievances, building up his hate, waiting for the time when he would become master of the village. With this meeting he had brought into motion something that no one could now stop. They continued to work on the bridge in the meanwhile. They worked with greater speed now that there was this threat of rain and floods. They were driving piles into the river bed. The previous week they had driven in the neighbouring set of piles. They then started to dredge, and while they dredged they had their first real rain storm. It started as a vast, black cloud that began to shift slowly across the sky. The birds left their perches on the trees. Somewhere in a nearby field a cow started to low.

'It comes so quickly, this storm,' said Armanis.

'I've left some bricks to dry. They'll be ruined,' said another. When the rains came they came as a great roar mingled with flashes of lightning. The only sound one heard then was a hiss, a continuous sloshing hiss as the greyish white sheet of rain rushed down absorbing and uniting the whole of the landscape, and as the cloud rolled on, spreading on and outwards, it darkened the sky and the entire scene sank into the gloom that the cloud had brought with it. The men had found temporary shelter under the trees where they cowered and huddled together. A short time before the break for the midday meal the rain began to ease up. Patches of brightness appeared in the sky, and the clouds dispersed.

A month later they held the pooja. It began late one might with only Girigoris, Heen Banda and his closest friends attending it. They sat around like mutes, their faces lit up like newly painted masks. The *kattadiya** danced quietly, fixed in a single spot, shuffling his feet and swaying his body. With a sudden lurch he would move forward, and with the flick of his wrist he would fling a powdery substance into the torch. The scene would explode in a glow of red brilliance and fiery yellows while the fire in the torch leapt violently into the air. The two drummers, fixed in their knee-bent, bow-legged stance, beat their drums, producing a drone now, then a throb. Suddenly, the *kattadiya* would swing into a whirl. He would spin around and around in a shifting axis. Everything would be exploding now, the drumming, the flashes of light, the leaping of flames, and slowly as the dancer became united in will with the drummer, those seated on the mats were knit into this intangible village will. They would soon be like owls on jungle trees while their shadows flitted nervously in elongated patterns behind them.

At the appointed time Girigoris took the tray of offerings and stood before the wooden altar, and throwing incense into a brazier he enveloped himself in a cloud of smoke. The roll of the drums

---

* exorcist

was louder now. He felt himself caught in the net of sound and
smoke and drawn into its flux, and in that moment the iron
entered his soul. The taut faces of his friends had grown more
intense suddenly. They had been shedding their identities slowly
and merging into a group, a tradition-bound village group. They
were bound together by their fears and turned into a pliable
instrument of destruction. Soon they would become so mindless
that they would have no separate wills, or the capacity to criti-
cally analyse any of their actions. For brief moments yet, certain
doubts and fears erupted in their minds, but having given their
will to do this thing they could not encourage doubts. They had
to snuff these as ruthlessly as they would do their deed. When
the last of them had stood before the altar and made his vow, a
man approached Girigoris and touched him on the shoulder.

'Come,' said the man, 'he's here now.'

Girigoris followed this man, a man not seen in the village
before. Girigoris was away a short while. One only heard voices
in the dark. Then he returned. He went out again, followed by
Heen Banda, Seetin, Armanis and the others, and they trooped
out into the darkness.

'The young man will meet us with the dynamite later tonight.
Till then we shall have to be on our own,' said Girigoris as they
went threading their way through the thicket in the darkness.

'What if the floods will not come as we expect?' asked a nervous
voice.

'That's a risk we must take.'

Arnolis, alone, of the neutral villagers, knew of what was to
take place. He sat in his hut brooding about it. He was unhappy.
At last, unable to stand it any longer, he arose, thinking he
would go and inform Andoris Rala. It was the least he could do.
He had not gone far before he met Davith Singho. He was moving through the dark in a kind of unnatural haste. So strange
for Davith Singho to be hurrying, Arnolis thought. 'At this time
of the night, whither do you go, Davith Singho?' he asked.

'I am returning from Andoris Rala's,' replied Davith Singho.

'It is to Andoris Rala that I go myself,' said Arnolis.

'Why do you go to Andoris Rala's?'

'It is about Girigoris and his friends that I go to tell him
about.'

'He already knows it. It is that I want to tell him about. They
were heading in the direction of the river more than an hour

ago.'

'It is well that he has been told about this. I can then return home.'

'You should be with Andoris Rala rather than at home, shouldn't you, Arnolis?'

'What then do you do yourself, Davith Singho?'

'I have not abandoned Andoris Rala. There are things I do and don't do. One does not go beating drums about it. These are things about which even a cowardly dog stiffens his back.'

'I am no coward, Davith Singho, but how can I or anyone get mixed up in these things about which no one knows which is right and which is wrong?'

'We are already mixed up in these things. There is no escape for those who run at a time like this. Such things as this grow so big that nothing escapes them.'

It is strange, most amazingly strange, thought Arnolis as he went his way.

In the meanwhile, two miles away, by the river, Girigoris and his men were alone in the dark, and they, by themselves, had to do their most uncommon deed. The stranger who had met Girigoris earlier was gone. He had done whatever he had to do and was gone. The others had to complete the task. They crouched there in the dark in two distinct groups. Bent on their strange task, they had, in some curious fashion, shed their human character. Girigoris waddled down there in his no-neck slouch. He went from one group to the other, stage-managing the undertaking.

'Has Seetin gone?' asked Girigoris.

'He must be there already,' said a voice. 'He went more than twenty minutes ago. He'll have no trouble fetching him out. We told him clearly what he had to do. The bait he'll offer will be strong enough to fetch him out.'

'Fools,' muttered Girigoris. 'To think it is enough to offer a white cockerel to the gods, as if that alone was enough. A human sacrifice is always better.'

'You do not intend to kill him, do you?' asked a voice in the dark.

'We must think of everything. We must do what the gods want. If it is a *billa** the gods want we can't refuse them, can we?

---

* human sacrifice

It will be so convenient—a river as turbulent as this, who can say how a man got into it?' Girigoris chuckled at his own joke.

Andoris Rala had risen earlier than the others to come to the river. He looked tired from the restless night they had spent. He stood on the bank. The platform on which the crane had rested had collapsed. The crane itself had tumbled forward, burying itself in the river, leaving a section of it rearing up in the sky. It was lying there like a wounded elephant that had crashed on to its knees leaving its giant buttocks and hind legs up in the air. The four cylinders in the centre of the river leaned unhappily, like men struck by paralysis. The dynamite had done its job only partially. Andoris Rala scowled at the river and pursed his lips. Floods coming on top of what happened in the night, would seem like the act of some crazy and irresponsible god. He shuddered to think of the horrible way Arnolis must have died. His thoughts went to other things now. There were many things he had to do before he left the village. Brampi was right after all. He had said this was a madness. It was a madness, a horrible madness that had come to the village. He stood there watching the turbulence of the river. It rushed on, waiting for nothing. It was just as well that the floods should come now. It would, perhaps, be the process by which the village might be cleansed of the madness.

Andoris Rala suddenly found Brampi standing by him. Andoris Rala turned and gave him a cold, distant smile and looked away.

'I have heard what happened,' said Brampi.

Andoris Rala said nothing. He just stared at the river.

'I was wrong not to have come last night,'

Still Andoris Rala said nothing. He stared into the distance and then he began to speak. He was addressing no one in particular.

'It's funny about this river,' said Andoris Rala. 'Ten years back the floods would not have come. Now every third or fifth year the floods come like the malarial fever used to come. Up on the hills they cut down the forest trees and throw the soil into the river. What else can the river do but overflow ? In the meanwhile the gods are the convenient *kathkarayo** who carry the burden of our ignorance.'

Brampi did not know what to say. Andoris Rala turned to look

---

* carriers

at him and then asked, 'Have you seen Davith Singho this morning?'

'No, I have not.'

'Doesn't he seem wiser than us all, Brampi? We all stood here and threw stones at him.'

Brampi stayed silent.

'Don't you think so, Brampi?'

'No, I don't. It is just cunning he has learned in the dock-yard.'

Andoris Rala smiled.

'This is what we all thought. I still say he is wiser than us all. He has learned the art of being apart from the foolishness of other people. When he can, he attempts to correct it. At other times he only laughs at it.'

Andoris Rala grew silent once more while the events of the night began to crowd in on his mind. He looked up at the sky. It had begun to darken again. The clouds banked up in great masses, steel grey clouds spinning and wheeling around.

'The strange and ill-fated bridge,' said Andoris Rala.

Brampi, standing beside him, looked at Andoris Rala's gaunt, tired face. It had changed in incredible fashion. It was not any longer the face of the man he used to know. It looked tired and old, wrinkles he had never seen before had suddenly appeared on the sunburnt face, but his eyes had this fierce glint in them, like in the face of a man who wanted to go on the rampage. He felt himself a stranger beside him. It was as if a barrier had come between them. Andoris Rala continued to stand there, saying nothing, just staring. Then he suddenly walked away as if he did not know that Brampi had been there by him.

It was almost three in the morning when the river burst its banks, the water surging and boiling and destroying everything in its path. Later, the villagers climbed to the top of the hill to have a better look at the devastation. Only the trees could now be seen, standing gaunt and silhouetted against the vast, glistening sheet of water. Andoris Rala had come with his wife to look at this. After some time he turned to his wife.

'Come, let us be gone from here. There's nothing we can do here.'

'Your field is under water and your paddy all drowned, don't you care about them?' asked his wife.

'Yes, I care about them. There is nothing I can do about them now.'

He was silent again as the two of them made their way carefully through the undergrowth—wet and dark, damp and cold. Their huts, and where they lived at least, were safe from the floods of destruction.

'I care about my paddy. Nearly half a year's labour gone,' he said as if the thought had returned to him. 'Yet this is not as bad when thought of against what else has happened here. We can once more grow these four acres of paddy, but when and how can we resurrect this village again to its old, decent and independent way of life. There was a time when evil could not rear its head as freely as it will now do. It's why I must go.'

As they went on they ran into Davith Singho. They stopped and felt awkward for a moment. They were still trying to understand each other. They had been suspicious of each other for a long time, and it would take some more time before they could meet each other without their past fears, but in their different ways they had established a bond.

'Is it very bad—the flood?' asked Davith Singho when he found his speech.

'Very bad. Man's mismanagement is sometimes called God's curse—*deiyange saarpey** they call it but they never call it *yakkungey dosai*.** The devil is always free of blame in such things. What do you hope to do after this, Davith Singho?'

'I do not know. Maybe I'll go back to the docks.'

Davith Singho did not know what more to say. But he asked, after a slightly painful pause, 'And what will you do, Andoris Rala, yourself?'

'I'll wander on and pitch my tent of leaves like the *ahikuntakayo* in a new place. The gypsies, the wanderers of the earth. I'll seek some place where the wind blows freely through the leaves.'

A week later, after the floods had receded, the villagers returned to the deserted bridge-site. In the lead was Girigoris, leading his men back to the scene of their crime. They came and gathered a short distance away from the river bank. They no longer looked like a harmless, farming peasantry. They had reduced themselves to the mental level of the next man and the man next to him and so on until they had acquired a peculiar uniform quality. It was the only way they could function as a

---

* curse of the gods; ** handiwork of the devils

pack. They stood there now looking at their handiwork. Girigoris raised his hand suddenly and held it out in the direction of the river. He still looked short and deformed and, curiously, like an anthropoid that had reared itself on its hind legs to charge at something, but there was this malignancy one felt now.

'Look,' he said, 'we didn't do it properly.'

His voice had a curious authority now. He had destroyed what more superior men had put up. It gave him this new sense of power. He was to lead the pack now. There was, in his eyes, as he looked at the men, a strange, never before seen intensity, as if in the mad rush of water he saw the fulfilment of his destiny.

'We thought the flood would finish it,' said Heen Banda, 'didn't we, Seetin?'

'A thing is always better when done to a finish. Remember that Heen Banda.'

'We can't have slipshod work in this village any more. We must discipline everyone.'

Heen Banda heard a confidence and self-assurance that he had not observed in Girigoris earlier. He felt a slight coil of fear stir in his belly. He did not know it as fear. He did not know what it was, he only felt, somewhere in the recesses of his mind, that it would be good for him to agree with Girigoris hereafter. The clouds began to drip on them suddenly, first as a drizzle, then as a light rain. Girigoris turned suddenly and moved away as fast as his short legs would carry him. The others turned too and started to move, infected by Girigoris' action. They had submerged their individual wishes into the group wish. When the leader turned they followed his example and turned themselves. They had become a pack. They began, then, to go at a trot, all moving together, a compact, tight little group.

Ranjini Obeyesekere

Despair

'No, it couldn't have been this car that you saw. You've made a mistake. I'm sorry,' Premini said as she closed the car's door with a click and started the engine. Then, as the car pulled away, she was suddenly aware of an answering click in her mind. Why, she had been to Colombo yesterday by train. It might have been possible. . . it just might have been. . . . She could not finish the phrase even in her own mind.

Confused images, phrases, places, names, things she had never before thought about, which she had not even been aware that her mind had registered, came crowding in on her. Each image seemed to buttress and support an earlier one, and brought with it new doubts.

It might be true. What the man had said could be true. The blood seemed to have burst into her brain leaving the rest of her numbed, ice-cold. She could not see where she was going, it was some time before she realized that for the past half-hour she had been going round and round a single block of houses.

The secure, not necessarily idyllic, but not unhappy, world in which she had lived these many years seemed suddenly to fall apart. The ground on which she had built her life had given way in a manner she had never expected. She had slipped suddenly into a yawning cavern of doubt. Doubt which she knew would never be dispelled because the facts could never be verified. Was it, after all, doubt, or a small, hard core of certainty? She did not know what to call it—she was only aware of its existence within her. But it could be lethal—that she knew. She could fight it but she could never destroy it.

She jammed on the brakes and was thrown forward with a jerk. A cart full of brightly coloured sweetmeats, decked with flies, was being trundled across the street by a nonchalant boy who seemed totally unruffled by erratic lady drivers. Jerked back into the external reality of the street, Premini took hold of herself. What was she doing? She had to collect clothes from the laundry, do the day's marketing, pick up her son from school. But all the while she had the sinking conviction that none of these things really mattered.

Her activities, the daily household chores, the children's routine, her work at the hospital, had all had—even though she never thought about it much—a kind of total meaning which gave point to her existence. Now, suddenly, by the accidental intervention of a total stranger—perhaps even a well-meaning one, this whole edifice had collapsed.

Her ego, that human ego, which blossoms in the surety of another's love, had shrivelled dry. She realized for the first time how dependent she had been on the knowledge of that love. Only if one rid oneself of the bondage of human affection could one rid oneself of this dependence. Wasn't that the meaning of the Buddhist doctrine?

But even as she accepted intellectually the truth of this premise, her whole being strained against its realization. For it was, after all, this very dependence, this belief in the strength of another's affection, that had given meaning and joy to her life, her home, her children, her work. This belief she no longer possessed, and with it went the joy that made daily life livable.

Yet nothing had changed in the last half-an-hour in the world around her. In spite of the turmoil within her, her conscious mind now began to function automatically, in full control. She parked the car near the market and got out. To anyone seeing her, she was the cool, collected lady doctor, dressed in a crisp voile saree, returning after the hospital rounds to do her usual day's marketing. She moved quickly and surely, threading her way through the Sunday morning crowds; bought the week's groceries, the meat, fish, vegetables and fruit. But even as she bought and paid, bought and paid, inside her was the persistent, insistent murmur: 'What for, what for, what is it all for?'

Mentally she listed her purchases. She must get it over soon, get away from here. The crowd, the smells, the hectic buying, selling, bargaining, were more than she could take. She had been one of them too. Only yesterday she had been one of these people, as involved in the immediate purchase, as immune to her fellow-shoppers, beggars, idlers, traders, stray dogs and vagrant children. Today she stood apart; alone, isolated, uninvolved, with an overwhelming feeling of the futility of it all, and a strange ironic pity for these others and herself!

Someone called to her from the crowd, 'Premini, how good to see you after all these years.' She turned and recognized a close friend of former days; they had been in medical school together. He had been recently transferred to Kandy. She turned to him. Suddenly she wanted to talk to him here in the market. Tell him everything—the truth about herself—that this frantic role she was playing had no meaning, no point at all. She wanted to cry, talk, tell someone, communicate her sense of total futility—but she was dumbstruck. 'Nice to see you, Tissa,' she murmured. 'I'll look you up some time. I have to rush now.' She turned and walked quickly away. Sobs seemed to be tearing their way up through her.

As she pushed blindly through the crowd, among the baskets, vegetables, litter and dogs, she stumbled and almost fell over the extended legs of a woman seated at the bottom of the stairway. Recovering, she glanced hurriedly at the woman to apologize, but the words died in her throat. The seated woman had not moved, but sat, legs extended, leaning her head against the wall behind her; her hair unkempt, her clothes in rags. What stopped Premini was not the squalor—that was normal in one's daily encounter with the market beggars. What struck her, even in her own preoccupied state, was the total immobility of the woman. She had not stirred.

Instantly, Premini had a searing vision of the cause. The woman was holding in her lap a child so thin that in all her experience as a doctor she had never encountered anything like it. The child lay on its back, its arms spread out, its tiny stomach distended, the skin stretched taut over its bloated belly. The child was dying, if not dead. And the mother knew it. Staring blankly in front of her, totally oblivious to every living thing around, she sat, statue-like, immobile. In one hand was a bottle with a dirty teat and a brown milk-like liquid which she held unseeingly to the mouth of the child. The child neither sucked nor moved. The mother sat, oblivious even of the child, aware only of the certainty of her own despair.

Premini stopped. An intense sympathy for this suffering creature, the depths of whose despair she instinctively sensed but would never plumb, overcame her. She bent quickly and emptied the contents of her purse on to the woman's lap, muttering: 'This child is very sick. Take him to the hospital soon.' Not a flicker passed over the woman's face. She remained unaware, unseeing, indifferent to human sympathy or help.

Premini almost ran to the car. Never before had she been witness to despair of such intensity. Not that she had not encountered death, suffering and grief in the hospital wards, on the streets, even in the market. Suffering was a part of her accustomed landscape. But here, for a moment, she had come face to face with total loneliness and the death of all love.

Premini's momentary empathy with the totality of the woman's despair seemed to have calmed her own agitation. There are, obviously, degrees even to despair, she thought ironically as she climbed into her car. She was late getting to the school and drove fast. But the immobile face continued to appear, a blurred vision on the windscreen. For once, for the first time perhaps in her life, she had truly experienced—even momentarily shared— another's grief. Perhaps her own experience of the morning had sensitized her.

Returning home, she felt drained out, desiccated by the day's emotions. She had to talk to someone. She turned to her son. 'I saw a woman today in the market with a very sick child—so thin it hardly looked like a child.'

'Did you take him to the hospital?' asked her seven-year-old logically.

Then it struck Premini that her response to the woman had been purely personal, emotional, private. She had made no attempt to help the woman or her child. And she was a doctor. After all, the child had not been dead. Something might yet be done. 'We'll go back and do just that,' she said decisively, turning the car back towards the town.

They drove fast. She knew it was urgent. She parked the car and ran in, making her way through the crowds to the stairway. She stopped short. She had not expected it. Both mother and child were gone. Gone, with her now-dead child no doubt, to lose herself in the anonymity of the human mass. For a moment Premini stood unmoving in the place where the woman had sat. It was as if she and the woman were one, fused together in a common isolation, a common desolation.

But even as she stood apart, looking out on the ant-like activity around her, she was aware that the intensity of her feeling was of that moment only. It would diffuse, dull and disappear. To-morrow, or the day after, or the day after, she knew, they would both again be part of the anthill.

Chitra Fernando

The Perfection of Giving

In my family, everyone regarded my father's elder sister as a very good and generous woman. I thought so too; in those days I had great respect for the opinions of my elders. Father said, 'Now try to be like Big Auntie, Mahinda. She's an example to us all.' Mother said, 'Big Auntie has more *shradda** than all of us.' Big Auntie never killed anything, not even a mosquito. And once I saw her saving some ants that had fallen into a basin of water; even the most insignificant creature benefited from Big Auntie's attentions. Big Auntie never stole; she had a large house and garden, a lot of jewellery and a small coconut property in Matara. She had everything she wanted. She never lied. She often said she never did, and of course, we all believed her. Big Auntie's conduct was always irreproachable. She was a broad woman, a bit on the short side and very dark; her nose and lips were thick, her skin coarse. She had a large mole on the tip of her nose and another with a hair in it on her chin. At the back of her head was a very small knot of hair. Unless they were her relations Big Auntie kept all men at a safe distance; and they kept her at an equally safe distance. She had never married. As for drinking or smoking—even the thought of her doing either of these things made me want to laugh.

Once Small Auntie caught Siripala and me sharing a cigarette in the back garden and the first thing she said was, 'How disappointed Big Auntie will be, Mahinda. You two boys are only fifteen, but you're already doing all these bad things!' Then she told Father about it. Father said, 'I will not have smoking, I will not have drinking in this house.' And then he told Big Auntie

---

* religious fervour

about it. Big Auntie looked at me in silence. She said, 'Mahinda, there's no need for me to tell you anything. Why should I say anything? Your own actions, your karma will deal with you. Smoke as much as you like. When you get lung cancer, you'll know all about it. This gratification of the senses brings only disease, death and *samsara**. Don't say I didn't warn you!'

Small Auntie, who was listening, nodded vigorously and said, 'I hope you've taken all this in, Mahinda. No need to look the other way! We're advising you for your own good.'

I often wished they were less concerned with my own good but I could say nothing. So I continued to look the other way.

Small Auntie was also unmarried and so had no household of her own. But though she was always singing Big Auntie's praises, she had a strange preference for living in our house. At the time of the cigarette-smoking incident, she was always talking about yet another instance of Big Auntie's generosity and compassion. Big Auntie's good deeds were uncountable so everyone was quite certain that at the very least she could be sure of a place in the Tusitha heaven. But this instance of Big Auntie's generosity was not an alms-giving; it was not a special pooja; it was not donating a loudspeaker to the temple for the relay of the daily sermon so that all the Payagala townsfolk could not but benefit from the loudness of Big Auntie's piety. This was a meritorious deed which was much better. Big Auntie was going to adopt a little girl from Matara! Not, of course, as a daughter. No one expected even Big Auntie to go to such lengths. It was unthinkable that a toddy tapper's child could be Big Auntie's daughter and, therefore, our relative. Big Auntie had to much consideration, too much common sense for that. She was a very practical woman. Kusuma was to come to her house as a servant.

Mala, my young sister, and I were at Big Auntie's house the morning she arrived. Kusuma, her father said, was twelve, but she looked about nine. She was small and skinny and her huge dark eyes half-filled her little face. Lice crawled in her curly black hair. There was a sore on her knee, in the village she had lived in a hut, one of eight children, half-starved, beaten and bullied. In Big Auntie's spacious house there was the comfort of good food, good clothes and a suitable wage deposited in a post office savings account. As Mother said, what more could any

---

* cycle of rebirth and death

sane servant expect! It was, we all felt, the perfect sum total of a servant's happiness.

Father said: 'That girl must have done a lot of merit in her past lives. Just imagine! After living like an animal in that hut to come to a house like Big Sister's!'

'Must be like heaven to her!' was Mother's contribution.

'She's not bad looking, and with all the good food she'll be eating she'll soon fill out. I hope she's not going to be greedy and steal. That must be firmly stopped, right from the start.' Small Auntie did her best to see that everyone observed the Second Precept*.

'Don't worry. Big Sister knows how to deal with stealing. She gives her servants so much! For them to misbehave is just raw wickedness, nothing else. As she always says so rightly, "No one can escape the karmic law," ' Father said firmly.

A week later, Big Auntie came to our house with Kusuma. Already we noticed an improvement in her appearance. Her hair was clean and lice-free. When she'd arrived she had been wearing a badly sewn shabby frock. Now she wore a close-fitting white cotton blouse and a pretty-flowered red-and-white cloth. Everyone complimented Big Auntie on the good work. She looked very satisfied.

'I know how to treat my servants. That's why they never leave my house. Salpi has been with me for fifteen years now.' This was perfectly true. Big Auntie did treat her servants well. They enjoyed a fair bit of comfort in her house. The full effect of Big Auntie's generosity to Kusuma appeared in about three months time. In that time she seemed to have grown taller, fairer and certainly much fuller. Big Auntie often said there was nothing wrong with her appetite. 'She eats as much as Salpi, and doesn't she love sweets!'

Small Auntie said, 'Now don't spoil her. I hope she won't steal. Have you caught her at it ever?'

'No. She's a bit greedy but I give her plenty to eat. So she really has no need to steal.'

'If she steals, will you beat her, Big Auntie?' asked Mala with interest.

'No, Mala. I don't beat anyone. You know that. I'll know what

---

* reference to the Five Precepts of Buddhism forbidding killing, stealing, lying, adultery and drinking

to do. I believe in the karmic law—it's my constant guide.'

I was sometimes puzzled by Big Auntie's way of talking about 'the karmic law'. Of course we all knew about karma. I remembered very well what the monk in the temple used to say: everyone had to take the consequences of his actions in one way or another. If you wanted too many things your desires would make you linger in *sansara*; you would be a prisoner of your desires. That's what the monk said. But I wasn't sure that I understood. Because Big Auntie, who was so wise, seemed to want a lot in return for whatever she did. But in those days I didn't bother too much about such things. I had so many more important things to think about like how to dodge *Pali** classes, or ways and means of smoking without being caught and lectured to.

Big Auntie was pleased with Kusuma. She was intelligent and learnt quickly. She soon learnt to be neat and clean. She was very helpful in the house. She dusted the furniture—all of Big Auntie's carved ebony chairs and couches in the sitting-room. She cleaned all the brass trays, lamps and vases. She was very good at fetching and carrying. Big Auntie wondered whether she should teach Kusuma to read and write. She thought about it a bit. Then she told us that to teach Kusuma how to crochet would be far more useful. Lace table-mats were in great demand and fetched a very good price. Big Auntie was a very practical woman.

After Kusuma's arrival, Mala began to visit Big Auntie almost everyday. Kusuma knew very little. So Mala began to feel very wise, though she knew very little herself. I was, of course, the really wise one among the younger lot. In those days, we all thought ourselves very wise. But everyone acknowledged Big Auntie to be the wisest. This was her own opinion as well—naturally.

It seemed to me that Mala liked showing off a bit. She would sit with Kusuma on the veranda steps and tell her all about the wonders of the world. Had Kusuma ever been to Colombo? No. Then she wouldn't ever have been in a lift, would she? No. Had she ever been on an escalator? No. Kusuma's ignorance was so satisfying to Mala! Had she ever been to the zoo? No. What was a zoo? Mala was in her element. She told Kusuma all about the zoo: the tigers, the lions, the bears, the giraffes, the kangaroos,

---

* the liturgical language of Buddhism

the zebras, the red-backed baboon, the elephants. Kusuma had seen an elephant! Oh! Mala was quite disappointed. Where had Kusuma seen an elephant? In a religious procession. That wasn't so bad. The zoo elephants didn't do anything so ordinary. They balanced on little stools or skipped round the arena, and then all the people laughed and clapped. Kusuma longed to go to Colombo to see all those marvels. She asked Mala a thousand-and-one questions. Mala brought her picture books. Kusuma had never held a book in her hands before. She turned over the pages carefully. Mala lent her the books for a few days. She couldn't read, of course, but she loved looking at the pictures. Then Big Auntie ordered Mala to take the books away. Kusuma looked at the pictures too often. That very afternoon she was looking at pictures when she should have been polishing the brass. Of course, Big Auntie didn't mind Mala talking to Kusuma. But she must not spoil her. So Mala took the books away. But Kusuma talked and talked about the animals in the zoo.

'The cat is like the tiger,' said Kusuma. 'It's a little tiger,' she added and cuddled the household cat.

'Yes,' I said, 'the cat is a kind of tiger.' And I told her all about cats and tigers and leopards. She listened to me with her great black eyes wide open. She had a great longing for learning, for knowledge, in those days.

The New Year drew closer. We were going to spend the New Year in Colombo with Fair Auntie and all our cousins. Mala asked, 'Can we take Kusuma too?'

Mother looked surprised. It was such a—such a new idea! She didn't know what to say.

'She's never been to Colombo. She's never been in a lift. She's never been on an escalator. And she's never seen a lion or a tiger or a giraffe, or a zebra or a kangaroo or a. . . ' Mala had to stop for breath.

'Big Auntie. . . Big Auntie. . .   began Mother.

'I'll ask her,' said Mala.

I decided Mala was a lot wiser than I had thought her. We went to Big Auntie's the next day. Mala carried a dish in her hand.

'What's that?' I asked.

'Um. . . nothing,' said Mala.

'Nothing! Let me see, let me see.' I lifted the cover of the dish and saw the mangoes inside. I laughed. I understood all.

'There's nothing to laugh about,' she said a bit huffily.

'Ah, Mala, what's that?' Big Auntie eyed the dish with great interest.

'We had a lot of mangoes at home. And I said you liked mangoes. So Mother sent it.'

Big Auntie smiled. She loved getting presents. Mala said to-morrow she would bring her some mangosteens. Tomorrow Banda would come from Kalutara and he always brought mangosteens at this time of the year. As we were leaving Mala said, 'We're going to Colombo for the New Year. Can Kusuma come too? Please, please, Big Auntie, please let her come. I always feel so bored at Fair Auntie's. Everyone's bigger than me and they don't play with me. Please, Big Auntie.'

Mala's pleading, almost tearful face—the mangoes of today, the mangosteens of tomorrow! How could Big Auntie refuse? She did not refuse. So it was settled. Kusuma would go to Colombo with us. Mala raced to the back of the house. Kusuma was sweeping the garden.

'You're coming with us to Colombo! You're coming with us!' Mala jumped up and down. She was mad with joy.

Kusuma stood where she was, quite still.

'You're coming to Colombo! To Colombo!'

Kusuma stared. Then all at once she understood. She smiled. A little dimple appeared for a moment. I had never seen that dimple before; I never saw it again. Her teeth were very small like gleaming grains of polished rice. And all the stars in the sky tumbled right into her great black eyes.

We were to go to Colombo the following week. The day before we left, Mala and I went over to Big Auntie's with the two bottles of honey that she had wanted. We were to leave for Colombo by the train the next morning. As we stepped on to the veranda we could hear Big Auntie's angry voice from inside.

'Aren't you thoroughly ashamed, girl? You eat a mountain of rice everyday. Yet you steal! Greedy, disgusting, filthy girl! *Chee! Chee!*'

Salpi said something but we couldn't hear her very clearly. Thoroughly curious now, we went into the pantry where all the noise was. The moment Big Auntie saw us she said angrily, 'Kusuma is not going to Colombo. She's not going. Don't I give her enough to eat? Do you know what she's been doing? Quietly eating my oil cakes. They were here in this airtight tin. I caught her stealing—caught her red-handed!'

It was true, Kusuma was clutching a cake in her hand. She stared at the floor.

'Half the cakes have been eaten! She's been stuffing herself these last two-three days. The greedy thing! Mala, you've been spoiling her with all this talk of Colombo—all these lions and zebras. She's getting quite disobedient. No Colombo for her, no new cloth and jacket. I give and give and give and is this my reward? This creature steals my cakes! Now what shall I do?'

'You can make some more, Big Auntie,' said Mala timidly. 'Look, we've brought you some really fine honey.' She held out the bottles eagerly.

Big Auntie ignored the bottles. 'Make some more! Oh! It's easy for you to talk! Will you make them for me? This fine young lady hopes to go to Colombo. And I'm to sweat over a fire making more cakes to replace those she's gobbled up! Oh, no! The karmic law is my constant guide. No Colombo, no zebras and kangaroos for this creature here. She'll stay behind and help to make more cakes!'

Kusuma didn't look up, didn't utter a word. The cake held tight in her clenched fist crumbled and the bits fell on the floor. Mala and I left quietly a few minutes later. We could still hear Big Auntie shouting at Kusuma. Tears of disappointment were streaming down Mala's cheeks; yet Kusuma hadn't shed even a single tear.

We saw her in the garden the next morning as we walked past Big Auntie's house to the railway station. Mala tried to speak to her but she ran inside. Mother said, 'Now, Mala, leave her alone. You'll only make Big Auntie angrier. It was very wrong of her to steal. She has to be punished.'

'Big Auntie's always talking about giving but she's not going to give Kusuma even a New Year present. And Kusuma isn't going to get any cakes, biscuits or sweets! Big Auntie is very mean!'

'Enough, Mala, enough. You talk far too much! Kusuma has stolen. She has to be punished. I agree completely with Big Auntie,' said Father severely. Mala pouted. She was glum all the way to Colombo. But when we arrived at Fair Auntie's, we found that our cousin Leela had come down from Kandy and then Mala forgot all about Kusuma.

After the cake incident, Big Auntie kept Kusuma very busy,

she was always cleaning, polishing, sweeping or crocheting. There was little time for play.

In the months that followed I too began to be increasingly busy. At the end of the year, I sat for my first public examination and passed. After that, I went to live with Fair Auntie in Colombo and went to the university there.

I still spent my holidays in Payagala—that small dull town! I remember that last long vacation in my final year at the university very well. Big Auntie was just the same—still full of *shradda*, still busy collecting meritorious acts. But there was now about her an air of relaxation! The air of someone who could rest a bit after a hard life of meritorious toil and labour. Big Auntie knew that she was still a long way from nirvana but she was in no special hurry to get there. She had no objection to remaining in *sansara* for a couple of eons or so, and she was determined to spend those eons as comfortably as possible. She had always been a very practical woman.

A week before my vacation ended we were all invited to a big chanting and alms-giving at her house. Big Auntie's chantings and alms-givings were always a great success. Everyone enjoyed themselves. For at least two days before, the house was full of people, bustle, talk, laughter, the smell of food. There was friendliness and good humour everywhere. This chanting and alms-giving was to be a really grand affair. Twenty-five monks had been invited. Kusuma, who was very artistic, was helping with the decoration of the chanting pavilion. I watched her as she worked. She was at this time about nineteen—tall, slender, light-skinned. Her hair was tied back in a big knot at the nape of her neck. Her face was fuller, rounder but her eyes were as huge as ever. She moved quickly, lightly. And then all at once I realized that Kusuma was a very beautiful woman. So I looked at her often. So did Big Auntie, but for very different reasons. During a chanting and alms-giving there were a lot of young men around. Big Auntie took her responsibilities very seriously. Seeing that everyone behaved in the proper way was the most serious of these responsibilities. Kusuma, in particular, was a special responsibility.

Kusuma wasn't even in the least bit frivolous. Salpi was quite old now, and Kusuma was beginning to have an increasingly important place in Big Auntie's household. She valued that importance very much. She moved gracefully but efficiently from kitchen to veranda, supervising, organizing, advising. One young man in particular was very willing to obey her instructions and orders. He always managed to find work where she was likely to be. If Kusuma was in the kitchen, he was there too, eager to cut, chop, sift or pound. If she was in the sitting-room, now cleared for the chanting pavilion, there he was eager to hammer in nails, paste paper, move tables and chairs. Kusuma spoke to him very briskly, sometimes even severely. There was never the slightest softness in her voice or face. But once I saw her look around as if searching for someone. She looked anxious. Then she spotted him among all the other young men and smiled, a quick, tiny smile. Big Auntie did not see that smile, but I did. I asked Mala who he was. 'Ah, that's Piyadasa. He works in Martin *Mudalali's* shop.' I looked at him again. He was tall and light-skinned and had a kind face. I liked him.

On the night of the chant, the twenty-five monks arrived in all their yellow-robed splendour, and took their places in the white pavilion. Its walls were made of cutwork paper; its canopy a dazzling white cloth. If the monks, who were seated inside the pavilion, looked up, they would have seen that the canopy had little bunches of young coconut leaves hanging from it at intervals. They had been placed there by Kusuma.

We sat around the pavilion on mats and listened to the monks chanting the sacred texts. I looked around me and noticed Piyadasa seated behind Kusuma. They were right at the back of the room. Big Auntie, who was the chief supporter of the temple and donor of everything, sat by herself on a special little mat right in front. She held her clasped hands high, almost at forehead level. She was the picture of perfect *shradda* and we all admired her greatly.

After the Great Chant, I went off to bed. Big Auntie sat listening to the chanting all night, I was told. This was nothing less than we expected. Yet she was the most energetic of us all the next morning. After the morning meal, the chief monk preached a short sermon. I still remember that sermon very well. It was on *danaparamita*, the perfection of giving. We had heard lots of Buddha's rebirth stories on the perfection of giving before: the story of Vessantara, of Siri Sanghabo, and of course the story of the little self-sacrificing hare whose image God Sakra placed high up in the bright moon for all to see. These stories we all knew. But not the story the chief monk told us that morning; this was new to us.

'Good people,' he began, 'of the ten perfections no one perfection is better than another. All these ten equal perfections reside in the Buddha, brighter than a thousand suns. Bearing this in mind, today I shall discourse on the perfection of giving. The perfection of giving shows itself in one key way: in generosity. Giving of alms is generosity. And those who seek the Supreme Goal must ceaselessly practise such generosity. Our good Payagala Hamine and all you others who have participated in this ceremony have shown your devotion to the Doctrine by your liberality and by your presence here. Yet, hard is the way to Enlightenment. Listen to this:

'Once a *bodisathva** was born a king, Manicuda by name. He was compassionate, generous, a giver and donor of all things. Being so, Manicuda wished to perform the great sacrifice, *nirargada*. Various heretics, Brahmins, mendicants, beggars, princes gathered for the great sacrifice. The *bodisathva*, Manicuda, addressed the assembly: "Sirs, I wish to perform the great sacrifice, *nirargada*, at which no doors are closed, no living being killed. Accept with minds full of sympathy these sacrificial gifts." And gifts were given to all those who came to suit their desires. Then, on the twentieth day, at sunrise, Sakra, the lord of all the gods, wishing to test the *bodisathva*, took the form of a terrible demon and arose suddenly from the great sacrificial fire. He cried out, "Fortunate and compassionate lord, deliver me who suffer severe pain by a quick gift of food."

' "Fear not, fear not, dear one, here is as much food as you desire."

' "It is not this kind of food I eat, great king, but the flesh and blood of the newly killed."

' "The kind of food you eat, dear one, cannot be had without injury to others. I abstain from killing. Therefore, eat my flesh and drink my blood to your content. Today, giving away my flesh and blood, I shall place my foot on the head of Mara**. Thus will I delight the whole world that yearns for liberation."

'As the *bodisathva* spoke, the whole earth trembled like a boat in the ocean. Gods, demons and deities, hearing of that wonderful gift, were alike spellbound.

'Taking a knife, the *bodisathva* opened a vein in his brow. The

---

* one preparing for Buddhahood; ** Death

demon drank, quenching his thirst. The *bodisathva* filled with delight, next cut off his flesh and gave it to the demon to eat. And he thought, "My wealth had been fruitful, my flesh, my blood, my life has been fruitful."

'As they read his thoughts, the gods assembled in the air cried aloud with joy. Sakra assumed his own form saying, "Great king, I am Sakra. What do you wish to gain by this deed, by this most strenuous effort?"

'The *bodisathva* replied, "Kausika, by this gift I do not wish to be a Sakra, a Mara or a Brahma or gain sovereignty over the universe or birth in the heavens. But by this deed may I attain perfect Enlightenment to release the unreleased, to console the unconsoled, to liberate the unliberated. This is my wish."

'This, good people is *danaparamita*, the perfection of giving.'

The monk stopped. The sermon was over. For a moment we were all silent. Then people stirred, joints cracked, and Big Auntie with hands clasped high above her head cried out in a voice trembling with *shradda*, '*Sadhu**! *Sadhu*! *Sadhu*!' All who were there took up the cry. The monks bowed their heads and gazed steadfastly at their fans. After giving the people his blessing, the chief monk, followed by the others, left.

Big Auntie, her face beaming, came up to Mother and Small Auntie.

'This is the most successful chanting and alms-giving I've ever given—everything went off beautifully! Did you notice how Mrs Welikala was eyeing the pavilion? It's ten times nicer than hers!'

Small Auntie laughed. 'She asked me who had made it and where we had got all that white paper from. I muttered something, but didn't tell.'

Both aunts laughed gleefully, almost like little girls.

Two days later, when I arrived home after a sea-bath, I found Big Auntie, Small Auntie, Mother and Mala all seated on the veranda talking. It seemed a very serious conversation. Big Auntie looked agitated, angry.

'Kusuma wants to marry Piyadasa!' Mala burst out when she saw me.

'Good idea!' I said approvingly.

Big Auntie stared at me as if I had suddenly turned into a serpent. 'Kusuma, marry Piyadasa?' she exploded.

---

* Hail!

'What's wrong with that?' I really couldn't see what all the fuss was about.

'That's what I thought too,' said Mala boldly. Mala had just got engaged to our second cousin, Nihal, and felt that everyone should be encouraged to marry as quickly as possible.

We both looked at Big Auntie. In spite of being a final year student at the university, I felt a bit afraid. Big Auntie's chest heaved, her lips trembled, her eyes seemed to shoot sparks of fire.

'The selfishness—the ingratitude of—everybody. After all I've—after all I've done. . . . '

Small Auntie said, 'You people—you young people these days don't think of anything serious. Only your own selfish desires matter. Do you ever think of your duty?' She spoke very severely.

'Lust, lust, lust, they're all filled with lust. When I think of what I've done for that girl! She was like a wild animal when she came to me. Covered with sores and lice! I cleaned her, fed her, clothed her, civilized her. . . Piyadasa came to me and said he wanted to marry her. . . said she was willing. I couldn't believe it. . . to do this thing behind my back!'

Big Auntie's chest began to heave again.

I said, 'Now, Big Auntie, don't be angry with me, but they haven't done anything behind your back. Piyadasa came and asked you, didn't he? They haven't run away or anything. As Freud says. . . . '

'Mahinda, what do you know about these things! After you went to that university, your head is stuffed full of useless foreign ideas. Who is this Freud, ah? Who is this Marx you're now always trying to talk about? What do these foreigners know of our ancient Sinhalese culture? I've given Kusuma so much! I've been a mother to her. Is it too much to ask for a little gratitude in return!'

'It's her duty to stay with Auntie. Big Auntie didn't bring her up for nothing!' said Mother.

'But she says Piyadasa and she will live close to Big Auntie. She says she'll continue to work for Big Auntie,' argued Mala.

'I know what those promises are worth!' Big Auntie sounded very sour.

'Will Kusuma have to live with Big Auntie forever then?' asked Mala.

'Why not?' snapped Small Auntie. 'Much better for her to stay with Big Auntie than go off with that Piyadasa and have ten children!'

'I'm not selfish. I'll arrange a marriage for Kusuma to the right person at the right time. But she can't marry Piyadasa.' Big Auntie was very firm about that.

'Arrange a marriage for her! No wonder she's so selfish. You've spoilt her thoroughly, Sister,' said Small Auntie.

'I'm going to ask Martin *Mudalali* to send Piyadasa away to his brother's shop in Galle. I've done a lot for Martin *Mudalali*. That man has a lot of respect for me.'

'What if Kusuma runs away?' I asked.

'She'll never do that,' said Mala. 'She's very loyal to Big Auntie.'

'Loyal! Fine loyalty!' snapped Big Auntie.

Kusuma did not run away. She continued to live in Big Auntie's household exactly as before. After a few months, Big Auntie forgot all about the Piyadasa incident. He eventually married a girl in Galle and, as far as we knew, never even visited Payagala again. Kusuma, of course, never married. I never heard Big Auntie talk about arranging a marriage for her again. But she gave over the running of the house entirely to Kusuma. This left her free to study Higher Philosophy. It was Kusuma who arranged for the sale of all garden produce like coconuts and yams. It was Kusuma who bought all the necessities for the household. It was Kusuma who organized all the chanting ceremonies and the alms-givings. She became almost as keen as Big Auntie in the performance of such duties. They seemed to give her an ever-increasing pleasure. She talked a lot about how the accumulation of merit would give a person a better life in the future. She often said that she must have been very wicked in a past life and was determined to be better in this, her present one. Big Auntie was very pleased with her. Small Auntie began to be almost jealous.

I was in Payagala for a few weeks before leaving to study further at London University. 'Mahinda,' said Small Auntie, 'I think Big Auntie gives Kusuma too much to do in the house. That woman is more the mistress of the house than Big Auntie herself. You should listen to her talking! I don't like the way she talks to me! She's turned into a very bossy woman. But Big Auntie listens to everything she says and does everything the way she wants it done. I don't like it.'

It was true that Kusuma occupied a very special place in Big Auntie's household. It was true that she spoke to us all as if she were our equal. There was nothing menial about Kusuma. But I didn't see why she should be menial. And I told Small Auntie so.

'You understand nothing, Mahinda, for all your book learning,' said Small Auntie. She sounded a bit annoyed. But since this is what everybody at home had always been telling me for a long time, I took no notice. I just smiled as I now always did, when they talked to me like that.

It was a very long time before I returned home again. Many things had happened during my absence. Big Auntie had a stroke which paralyzed both her legs. She now used a wheelchair. After Small Auntie's death of a heart attack, Mother had sold our house and gone to live with Mala in Kandy. Mala urged me to go and see Big Auntie, who still lived in Payagala. 'Kusuma looks after her very well—Big Auntie is so lucky to have her—but she's very lonely. I haven't been to Payagala for over a year. I'm tied to the house with all these children.'

'Yes, yes, go, Mahinda,' said Mother. 'I went to see her last year when I was in Colombo, but you know how difficult travelling is these days. The trains are jam-packed. And I'm too old to knock about now. Go, Mahinda, she'll be so happy to see you. She's very fond of you.'

Big Auntie's house was still the same. The garden looked flourishing. The coconut trees were loaded with nuts, the mango trees with fruit. The orchids just beside the veranda were all blooming. Big Auntie was in her wheelchair on the veranda. She saw me, tried to speak, but couldn't. Her face quivered. I went up to her and took her hand. She held it tightly. Her hair was completely white, the skin of her neck and arms hung down in loose folds. In the years I'd been away, she had shrunk into an old, old woman.

'I thought I'd never see you again, *putha**,' she said at last. Her voice was all quavery. 'When did you return?'

'About three weeks ago. Payagala is exactly the same.' We talked for a bit. I gave her news of Mother and Mala. She listened. There was a pause. I said, 'So, tell me what you've been doing all these years, Big Auntie.'

She brightened up. She told me she'd bought half an acre of land next to the temple grounds and had built a new preaching hall there. Kusuma had paid for the whitewashing with the money she earned from crocheting table-mats and pillow lace.

'She's a good girl—doesn't spend her money on clothes and powder like some women. Her one aim in life is to do meritorious acts.'

'Because she wants to be born a rich woman in her next life?' I asked, smiling.

'What's wrong with that? We all want to better ourselves, don't we?'

I couldn't argue with that. 'Well, what other good deeds has Kusuma done?' I asked, mainly to soothe Big Auntie, who was now looking troubled again.

She said that two years ago Kusuma had donated a magnificent brass lamp to the temple. Big Auntie had wanted to contribute something towards it but Kusuma had refused very firmly. The merit from this act had to be hers and hers alone; she didn't want to share it with anyone.

'You must be very proud of all the good things Kusuma's been doing. You brought her up, so the credit is all yours.'

'Yes,' she said quietly. She looked down at her hands. I felt something was wrong.

'Aren't you happy with Kusuma, Big Auntie?'

'Yes, yes, I am, Mahinda. Very happy. It's a great joy for me to see how good she is.' There was a pause. 'Kusuma—Kusuma is building a new shrine-room.'

'Kusuma building a shrine-room! Kusuma! But where does she get the money from?' I asked, quite thunderstruck.

'She gets some money from the sale of her table-mats and pillow lace. Then there's the coconut money.'

'But the coconuts belong to you?'

'I asked her to use—to use the money,' said Big Auntie uncomfortably.

We were silent. I looked around. I could see into the sitting-room from where I was. It seemed strangely bare. Something was missing. Suddenly it came to me. Big Auntie's antique ebony furniture!

'What has happened to your ebony furniture?'

Big Auntie looked even more uncomfortable. 'I asked Kusuma to sell it—to sell it for—for the shrine-room.'

---

* son

'But Big Auntie, that—that furniture—you loved that furniture! You said you'd never sell it.' In fact, she had always said that the furniture was for me because it had belonged to my grandfather. I wondered whether she remembered. I looked at her. She was twisting her hands nervously. 'Kusuma has been like a daughter to me. She does everything for me.'

'Where is Kusuma?'

'She's at the temple. She goes everyday to see how the building is going on. Don't say anything—don't scold her, Mahinda. She's like my daughter. Her one desire in life is to build that shrine-room.'

'But at your expense! Did you really want to sell that furniture?'

Big Auntie began to weep. 'That furniture was my father's. I wanted you to have it.'

I have never seen Big Auntie weep before. Great rivers of tears streamed down her shrunken cheeks. I noticed she wasn't wearing her ruby earrings. I didn't need to ask what had happened to them. I supposed all Big Auntie's jewellery would be gradually sold to pay for the shrine-room and other meritorious acts.

'I don't want the furniture. I live in a tiny two-roomed flat in London, the size of your sitting-room. What could I do with ebony furniture there?'

'I don't want to cling to my possessions. But that ebony furniture was my father's. I didn't want to sell it.'

'Never mind, never mind, Big Auntie. Building a shrine-room is a very good thing, a very meritorious act.' It seemed strange to be talking like that. But I couldn't really console Big Auntie, though she stopped weeping.

It was almost lunch-time when Kusuma returned from the temple. She was not at all pleased to see me. I could see that. She was now a middle-aged woman—broad, strong, determined, hard. Lunch was served almost immediately. I wheeled Big Auntie's chair to the dining-table. Big Auntie had loved good food in the old days. I looked at the rice, the coconut *sambol* and the bit of dried fish on the table. Kusuma stared at me defiantly, as if daring me to criticize. I was silent. Big Auntie said, 'If only I'd known you were coming, *putha*! I'd somehow have got some seer fish and prawns for you. You used to like then so much!'

'Now I like dried fish better than anything else,' I said, giving her a bright, false smile.

It was a very silent meal. I wondered whether I should tell Mother and Mala about Big Auntie's plight. But what good would it do? It was impossible for Big Auntie to live in Kandy. There was no room for her in Mala's house. And who would look after her? I just could not see Kusuma living in Mala's household.

As Kusuma was clearing away the dishes and plates I said, 'So, Kusuma, I hear you're building a shrine-room. It must be a very expensive business.'

Big Auntie looked at me pleadingly, fearfully.

Kusuma glared at me. 'I have found the money for it. It's a very meritorious deed. No one should interfere with such a good thing.'

'When will it be completed?'

'The building will be complete in about a month's time. But I need more money for the image and the wall-paintings inside. My name will be inscribed outside because I am the donor,' she said smiling, proudly, for the first time. 'Would you like to donate something, Mahinda *Mahattaya*?' she asked.

I was surprised. Big Auntie looked at me appealingly. I pulled out my purse and gave her fifty rupees. She took it eagerly and put the notes into her purse.

I wheeled Big Auntie back to the veranda. 'Tell me about London, *putha*. Is it a big city? England must be a very advanced country, no? Who cooks for you?'

She laughed when I told her that I cooked for myself.

'Fine meals you must be cooking! No wonder you look so thin. So why don't you get yourself a wife? Then she can cook for you.'

I ignored these suggestions and got up saying I had to leave. Her face changed. '*Arre*, *putha*, what's the hurry? Stay the night, stay the night.'

I said I couldn't. I had to be in Colombo for a lecture at the university that evening. And I'd promised Mother to be in Kandy the next day.

Big Auntie gave a little sigh. 'When shall I see you again, *putha*? Next time you come, I'll be dead.'

'Don't talk like that! Next time I see you, you'll be on your feet and running this house yourself!' But neither of us believed in that extravagant lie even for a second.

She tried to smile, then said, 'No, I'll die in this wheelchair.

It's my karma. But I'm very lucky to have Kusuma—she's like my own daughter. It's my karma,' she repeated.

I said goodbye. She clung to my hand and kissed it. 'Come and see me again before you leave, *putha, Tun sarane Pihitai**!' And she said once again, 'It's my karma.' A commonplace, almost meaningless phrase mouthed by so many. And yet, as I looked back for one last wave, there seemed to be a truth in it—a truth reflected in that heavy, sullen woman standing in the doorway, so like the other feebly waving a loose-skinned hand.

---

* the blessing of the Triple Gem, a Buddhist blessing

J.S. Tissainayagam

Misunderstanding

Bandula was waiting at the bus-stand after his lecture to go home. The day was bright and cool. The sky was pale blue overhead, with a dense mass of white clouds with grey undersides forming on the horizon, partially hiding the grey hills. Behind him lay the river, a muddy yellow, spattered with glistening silver ripples.

Bandula was in his second year at the university, and proud of where he was. He was not well off; but he managed to make ends meet somehow; he shared a room with two others and stinted on superfluous expenses, and sometimes even on meals. Still, he found university life tolerably happy, and had very little to complain about.

It was chilly at the bus-stand and there was no one to talk to. Feeling bored, he stretched his hands and yawned. It was then that he saw her coming.

Sherine was in The English Medium. One always said The English Medium, and not the English medium, at the university. She was one of the few, the happy few who had the privilege of being in it, where you were at once envied and hated by the other students. She herself did not attach much importance to that. After all, what was in it? She was proficient in English, which enabled her to follow lectures in that language. Others proficient in other languages followed them in the languages they knew. That was all. But there was pride deep within her. It was bred from the attention she got from the other students. She was conscious that, after all, everybody could not be exclusive.

Sherine always ran the last few yards down the slope out of the university gates. She always felt like a prisoner escaping past the last outpost and into freedom when she did that. The canteen was near the gate and there was generally a crowd of students chatting around there. As she walked down now everybody stopped talking and stared at her. Some of the boys whispered amongst themselves, and others laughed uproariously to attract attention to themselves. The girls, of course, merely gave her a hostile glance. Sherine looked steadily at the ground. She hated people scrutinizing her like that. It made her feel nervous and embarrassed. A few weeks ago, when ragging was on, her body used to stiffen with fear when she heard boys making catcalls or hissing behind her. But at least that time was past and its aching fears were now no more. But still her nervousness and diffidence lingered. Hearing the whispering now, she thought to herself how silly these boys were. What was so special about her? But then a wave of pride swept over her; she was in The English Medium---an object to be idolized by the boys and envied by the girls.

Bandula saw her coming and instinctively smoothed down his well-oiled hair and pulled up his collar. He looked at her with the corner of his eye, and, assuming a nonchalant expression, started kicking the grass by the wayside and stared across the river. But he did not see the flowing river or the banks mantled with little yellow flowers on the other side. Instead, he saw the image of the girl reflected on the dark water. She was above average height, broad---almost fat; but she did not move with the slow, indolent movement of fat people; her steps were firm and her strides elegant. Her hair was cut short and her nose and mouth were small. She wore large, 'mod,' wire-rimmed glasses which gave a strange light to her big, beautiful eyes. She had an air of calmness and restraint about her; but with it, there seemed a touch of haughtiness and independence of spirit. The duality fascinated Bandula. Altogether, she looked a young, self-possessed mother, rather than an eighteen-year-old university student.

The girl arrived at the bus-stand, and after giving him an uninterested look, stared in the direction from which the bus would come. He had always wanted to rub shoulders with the girls of The English Medium; but there had always been constraints. His greatest fear was that he could not manage perfect English. He could speak in Sinhalaese easily, but, after all, it was not like using *Kaduwa**, was it? He could manage expressing

---

* Sinhalese for 'sword', term used by the Sinhalese-educated to designate English as a weapon of power and oppression

himself in English with some difficulty, but felt very awkward when doing so. Should he speak to her? After all, she was only a fresher, he a senior. Perhaps through respect for one in the second year she might not cut him dead. Bandula was not habitually shy; but these were extraordinary circumstances—addressing a girl in English. At last he drew a deep breath—it was now or never—and screwing up his courage, asked in a muffled voice, somewhat louder than needed, 'Bus service bad, no?'

Sherine started at that; a sudden loud baritone from so close. His accent was coarse, like one unused to speaking English. Sherine was confused at first, but answered, 'I don't know. I've only been here a little while.'

'Uh?' asked Bandula. She spoke very fast and he found it hard to follow.

She glanced at him briefly, and Bandula thought that though she was not strictly beautiful, she had a charming air about her.

'I said I've been waiting only a very short time.'

'Yes, yes,' said Bandula, and grinned.

There was a pause. He walked about trying to think of another topic of conversation.

Then, he asked, 'What subjects are you doing?'

At this, Sherine turned, the sun glinting on her specs as she did so. She found him staring seriously at her, as if performing a task that required immense concentration. The way he spoke was peculiar too. It was too fast—the words gushed out of his mouth as if he were delivering a prepared speech. He was tall and thin, and clean-shaven, which was almost an exception at the university. Seeing her look at him, he smiled. He had rather uneven teeth, slightly yellowed through excessive smoking. But to Sherine his mouth seemed to overflow with large, filthy teeth; his pink gums seemed to provide a sharp contrast to their dirty yellow. Sherine turned away in disgust, and replied, 'English, Classics, Politics.'

To Bandula her tone seemed flat and lacking warmth. He had done nothing to her, then why was she reacting this way?

But Sherine was rather a timid girl and her nervousness rose. Why was this boy asking her these questions? She had escaped being ragged, and heaved a sigh of relief after the Freshers' Night was over. She looked at him apprehensively. He looked mild and harmless---a nice guy, she thought to herself. But then she remembered his filthy, discoloured teeth. It showed he lacked polish. That little something separated him from her. But still for all that he seemed sincere—quite a contrast to some of her batch-mates in the English medium, from Royal or St Thomas', who thought no end of themselves.

Bandula was now at his wits' end. How could he make this girl talk? His friend Lalith had told him that the only way was by ragging the girls. But Bandula knew that Lalith had a complex. He came from a family that was rich. His father, who had origi-nally been a boutique-keeper, had made money in the timber business and even owned a small car now. Lalith had money, and was easily the best dressed in their batch; but he lacked one accomplishment that would have permitted him to hobnob with the elite—his English was very poor. He had come to the univer-sity glad of the opportunity to learn English; but his natural waywardness had done nothing to improve his knowledge. So now he posed as a staunch nationalist, hating the English-speak-ing classes bitterly, and trying to humiliate them in whatever way possible.

But Bandula was different. He came from a home with a pious Buddhist background, and that, along with his naturally mild temperament, made him dislike harming other people. He had been one of the few who had not ragged the freshers that year. Of course he too had a desire to climb up the social ladder; but unlike Lalith, with him it did not amount to an obsession.

But the immediate problem was to think of a new topic of conversation, something where a dialogue of some length was possible. Bandula racked his brains. Suddenly, he had it!

'Lunch—you go home?'

It took Sherine a few seconds to grasp that. She replied, 'Yes,' feeling her heart begin to thump again.

'I eat in canteen,' he stated, 'food very bad, but what to do—no?' He spoke jerkily, declaring rather than saying his words. It was as if he had no control over his vocal cords. He contin-ued, 'They must make canteen private. Then good.'

For the first time, Sherine's curiosity overcame her fear. 'What do you mean "private?" '

'Private owning,' said Bandula, gesticulating vigorously with his hands; he was delighted that the girl was taking some interest in what he was saying. Sherine, on the other hand, noticed that when he spoke his face assumed an expression of almost pain-ful intensity.

Actually, Bandula ate his lunch at the canteen always, and he liked the food too; but he knew that most Colombo-folk went to restaurants and night-clubs regularly—like in all the films he had seen. This girl must be used to big hotels too. So he thought he would sound impressive if he could show that he was also familiar with top-class private hotels. He hoped fervently, though, that the girl would not repeat to somebody that he advocated private enterprise; he knew it could affect his position in the Party.

'Er. . . I suppose so,' said Sherine, trying to sound noncommittal. But her anxiety increased. Why was he asking about the canteen? Was he trying to make her say something that he could relay to the other seniors which would provoke anger and opposition? Oh God, she thought in despair, only if the wretched bus would come! She looked around. They were the only people at the stand. At least if the other girls would come it would be all right. A few minutes passed. Then, suddenly, she sensed him moving closer to her. What was he up to. . . ?

But Bandula's sharp ears had caught the sound of the approaching bus and he was only walking up to stop it. His heart was full of misgiving. Why would she not talk? Why was she so cold and withdrawn? Was it because he was not nice-looking? Surely that could not be?

When the bus arrived, Sherine gasped in relief. As she got in she saw the boy cough loudly and spit. Then he got in too.

In the bus, Bandula made one final, desperate attempt at starting a conversation. 'I will buy your ticket?' he inquired rather hesitantly, afraid of taking liberties. But he had seen in films, boys buying girls their tickets, after having spoken to them for only a few minutes. Surely this girl must be used to it.

Sherine was shocked and confused. But she brightened, remembering that she travelled by a season-ticket.

'I've a season. Thank you,' she answered in a clear, firm voice. She opened the exercise book in which she usually carried her season but found it was not there. Mildly surprised, she searched the next, and her pockets too, but it was missing. In consternation she remembered that it had been between the pages of a book she had lent to a friend that day. Well, she had to buy her ticket with the money she had, that was all. Then, in alarm, she remembered the boy who had offered to buy her a ticket. What would he think? He would think her a liar and despise her.

Cautiously, she looked around; there he was, well forward, with his back to her, digging into his pockets. In relief, she positioned herself in front of the conductor so that he would not see her buying the ticket. But the conductor did not have change; he gave her the ticket but said that he would hand over the balance later. Sherine sat down.

The tension she had been under for the last few minutes began to relax. She thought about him in a calmer frame of mind. His English was definitely very poor. She had also noticed certain detestable manners, like spitting on the road—and who knows, she thought, he might even be blowing his nose and wiping his fingers on leaves. Those habits she simply hated. He had no polish; that was evident. Then she remembered his hideous teeth. Then it suddenly flashed upon her that he was a human being too. Only, he had been raised in different circumstances from hers. That was all that divided them. The next time, she thought, she would go and speak to him, or at least smile at him without her silly earlier prejudices. But she did not realize that the flash of insight she'd had into his humanity was a fleeting thing, and that the conventions of society and the prejudices of class that had always conditioned her would return and blacken and stunt her mind.

Bandula waited for the conductor to come for him to buy his ticket. A few minutes passed and he looked back to see where he was. He saw the conductor give a few coins to someone. Casually, he glanced at the recipient—it was the girl. For a few seconds he found nothing extraordinary about that. Then suddenly it exploded in his mind that she would be only getting a balance if she had paid her fare. For a moment his mind went blank—then bitter rage replaced it. He was generally a calm, even-tempered young man; but now his placid face was dark with anger, and the thin nervous hands that held his books trembled. For even habitual mildness can be ruffled when one is slighted by a woman. It was ultimately his pride and self-importance that mattered to him most. After all, he was someone; and like most men he was acutely sensitive to criticism by women. He felt that the girl had insulted him. And a taunt from a woman is many times worse than any humiliation a man could inflict. Bandula did not love this woman, or desire her in any way; he had only wanted to measure his own worth by her standards. It was his ego that suffered.

The dirty bitch, he thought bitterly; just because he did not come from Colombo, did not go out dancing, or speak *Kaduwa*, she despised him and would not talk to him. It was not only she, but all those dirty bitches. This was their superiority. But what irked him most was that he would have to put up with their snobbishness and the airs they gave themselves. He was not one to indulge in self-pity. And as he pondered darkly, he decided that he could not let things be like that. He had to make her his equal. And he knew he could cut her down to size only through one means—by ragging her. That was the only way—to rag them till they cried for mercy. But the ragging season had been over weeks before, and the thought that now he would not get his revenge infuriated him still more. How right Lalith had been, he thought now, how absolutely right.

He bought his ticket and sat down. He sat opposite Sherine. The aisle divided them. It seemed now an unfordable gulf.

Patrick Fernando

Folly and Wisdom

Though her mind was rather small and its thoughts were quite
    absurd
She had a voice of honey, walked as lightly as a bird;
Since his heart was not too deep and was easy to be stirred,
He took her at a moment's glance, on first hearing her word.
If years had lent them learning now, they both might have
    preferred
That he had been less easy, that her voice had gone unheard.
But still her mind is rather small, still there's honey in her word,
And he is still too gentle to observe that he has erred;
And so the strength of age proves weak and bitterness is blurred.
But wiser men observing this are crazily disturbed,
Exalted eagles drop to earth to chide the sparrow bird;
They are clumsy at this level, incongruous, absurd,
The sparrows hop and wink and chirp, 'But how could we have
    erred,
We who in spite of all you say are not yet embittered?'

Patrick Fernando

The Late Sir Henry

Behind the usual friends and callers, Death
Slunk in and took this fine knight unawares.
Yet self-possessed he lies though robbed of breath
And reft of horses, mills and gilt-edged shares.

Two candles light the still impressive head,
Two more the feet, once of a scampering boy.
Sustained with eau-de-cologne the daughters shed
Tears wrung from memories of childhood joy.

We watched distinguished mourners congregate,
The hall being full, beneath a blooming tree,
And lighting their cigarettes, speculate
Beyond the mere margins of mortality.

Like disciples before Resurrection—
Bankers, brokers, objective though distraught,
Assessed the impact of the sudden loss upon
Politics, trade, industry, Church and sport.

At the graveyard gates boys were trying to sell
Ice-cream and oranges to cool that crowd
Arrived in thousands to observe how well
Sir Henry had assumed his sudden shroud.

With good manners for grief, every man in place,
And the weather fine, the rank chemistry
Of the flesh seemed foolish in this case;
Unthinkable the worm's brief ministry.

No wonder then the bell seemed shy to toll,
And priest apologetic as he sang
A final plea for the departed soul
And dropped the first clod with a nervous hand.

Lakdasa Wikkramasinha

To My Friend Aldred

My dear Chap,
In this Kandyan weather there is
no shame in having in your bed
a servant maid—
the same passion moved others too, famous in time—
when there were servant maids about;

   Achilles for one—who gave his heart to
Breseis, a milky slave.
and Tecmessa: enemy blood, as Horace has it;
and Agamemnon fired Troy and burnt his heart to a
cinder, hot for a virgin there:

   and 'though we do not get so Greek here,
we are not to such titillations immune
—being classical in our traditions.
And so it is
with you and your Jose
with such long lashes
to whom you have lost your heart.

   And no fear, she is not
engendered by the low
at all. Dismiss
the mere thought; I envisage indeed
such an ancestry
as leading in its heyday
to some king of these parts, or some
noble lord, or at the least

some lonely Scotsman in these hills. Else
she would not have such a loyal, unmercenary mind,
or cook such yams, steaming purple
and pots of jak, steaming yellow
or have a figure

straight out of the old poetry books:
Breasts like gourds, and ripe and Oh
nodding like geese. Thighs
like plantain trunks, and Haunches as a king could ride
on, or Keyt!

And lastly
in this matter of praise, in your fortune—
thick, black coils of hair on her head, and Elsewhere—
I mean, all's well
that ends there

And all roads leads to Rome!

Lakdasa Wikkramasinha

Don't Talk to Me about Matisse

Don't talk to me about Matisse, don't talk to me
about Gauguin, or even
the earless painter Van Gogh,
and the woman reclining on a blood-spread. . .
the aboriginal shot by the great white hunter Matisse

with a gun with two nostrils, the aboriginal
crucified by Gauguin—the syphilis-spreader, the yellowed
    obesity.

Don't talk to me about Matisse. . .
the European style of 1900, the tradition of the studio
where the nude woman reclines forever
on a sheet of blood.

Talk to me instead of the culture generally—
how the murderers were sustained
by the beauty robbed of savages: to our remote
villages the painters came, and our white-washed
mud-huts were splattered with gunfire.

Yasmine Gooneratne

The Peace-Game

'Peace' was a game we liked to play
as kids of six, or maybe seven,
it needs some players to divide
into two teams, of Odds and Evens
The Odds were the children down the street
and miscellaneous scraps and strays,
the Evens were my brothers and
our friends, swell, upright, regular guys.

'Peace' was the prize the game was fought
(or played, perhaps I mean) to win.
Their object was to keep us out
and ours to get, and then stay, in
for since our fathers didn't want
rough-housing near the orchid sheds,
we fought our battles over their
parents' vegetable beds.

We Evens were a well-fed lot
and tough, so that the little patched
and scrawny Odds would never dare
to say the teams were not well matched.
That was the beauty of the game,
we chose the ground and made the rules,
they couldn't really do a thing
about it, stunted little fools,

Except to put up quite a fight
sometimes, against our guns and such.
We called the entertainment 'Peace'
or 'War'—I can't remember which. . . .

Yasmine Gooneratne

Migrant Poet

Behind him a Kingdom sliding to decay
dragging with it lost childhood, sheltered youth
Before him alien shores, an unknown bay,
another Vijaya* he ventures south.

A strange bird dreams on a dry bough; marsupials
lift liquid eyes in silence, questioning
a stranger's footfall. Here no leopards snarl—
do beasts turn also from the pain of living?

And is this pleasant landscape, then, to be
the chosen setting for his spirit's death,
the hammering media's brash mythology
to breathe on him immobilizing breath?

Somewhere in this enchanted woodland brims
the secret well; and there her golden thread
his lost Muse sits and spins, and as she spins
the fallen blossoms listen for his tread.

False step to east or west, and desert grows
between these two. Look, landward from the sea
light footprints lead, through glades alive with shadows:
Others have passed this way ahead of me.

---

* mythical founder of the Sinhalese race who came as an exile from India

Perhaps in a lost age another kindled
here, in this glade, from that bird's dip and flight
or from the shape the moon took as it dwindled,
bright myth to lie beside on a cold night

or built a legend he could crawl into
and warm his blood to health and fruitfulness.
Lost myths, turned rubble now beneath the new
towering chainstore, rammed under the express-

way. I, a wanderer in this land,
turned by necessity to new material
strange to my eyes, uncertain in my hand,
shall I be fortunate enough to call

into forms unimagined in my youth
new life? Create in joy, here, on Death's lip?
Another Vijaya, I venture south
here to reshape my art, refit my ship.

Anne Ranasinghe

At What Dark Point

Every morning I see him
Sitting in the speckled shade
Of my blossom laden *araliya* tree
Which I planted many years ago
In my garden, and the branches now
Have spread into our lane.
Under my tree in a shadow of silence
He sits, and with long skeletal hands
Sorts strands from a tangle of juten fibres
and twisting twisting twisting makes a rope
That grows. And grows. Each day.

Every morning I pass him. He sits
In the golden-haze brightness under
The white-velvet fragrance of
My tree. Sits
On the edge of his silence twisting
His lengthening rope and
Watching
Me.

And seeing him sit day after day,
Sinister, silent, twisting his rope
To a future purpose of evilness
I sense the charred-wood smell again,
Stained glass exploding in the flames
(Fireworks of fractured glass
Against the black November sky)
The streets deserted, all doors shut

At twelve o'clock at night,
And running with animal fear
Between high houses shuttered tight
The jackboot ringing hard and clear
While stalking with the lust for blood

I can still hear
The ironed heel—its echoing thud—
And still can taste the cold-winter-taste
Of charred-wood-midnight-fear.
Knowing
That nothing is impossible
That anything is possible
That there is no safety
In words or houses
That boundaries are theoretical
And love is relative
To the choice before you.

I know
That anything is possible
Any time. There is no safety
In poems or music or even in
Philosophy. No safety
In houses or temples
Of any faith. And no one knows
At what dark point the time will come again
Of blood and knives, terror and pain
Of jackboots and the twisted strand
Of rope.
And the impress of a child's small hand
Paroxysmic mark on an oven wall
Scratched death mark on an oven wall
Is my child's hand.

Anne Ranasinghe

The Face Of God

Under the lamp that's on my desk
A lizard nightly waits to catch
The moths that come to dance their dance
Of death.

He watches them with golden eyes
Protruding from his naked head
While I watch him—his tense-poised stance
And single minded concentration
And then the sudden pounce and snap
Without the slightest hesitation
All in a brief pulsating beat
Of time.

A flickering of his blood-red tongue
And of the weaving dancing thing
Nothing is left except a wing
Projecting from his tight-clamped mouth
And a thin
Dark shadow
Seen through his transparent skin.

Thus for the moth the lizard's act
Is God and irreversible—
A final and accomplished fact.
I ponder his reptilian grace
Detachment and repulsiveness
And wonder of what God the face
That I shall see upon my death.

Peter Scharen

In the Renaissance of My Life

In the Renaissance of my life
black-and-white films made in the concentration camps
were shown, Dachau, Buchenwald,
images and books fell like lead.

In the Renaissance of my life
the Cubans had fought their revolution;
the poor studied and with doctors
and administrators worked the plantations.

In the Renaissance of my life—
Fanon had worked to death, Lumumba killed, then
heroic Che crucified
on metal, his dead face
soaked in the brine of that photograph.

In the Renaissance of my life
Lyndon Johnson and the Pope lived well and poked
each other in the ribs
and blessed the world,
Mao blessed Nixon blessed the presidency blessed Brezhnev,
all blood-smeared.

In the Renaissance of my life
millions starved, millions exterminated,
black millions, browns, yellows,
millions who would have died anyway,
their bodies sprawled across the T.V. sets.

IN THE RENAISSANCE OF MY LIFE
I ENTERED THE LAND OF THE PIG.

In the Renaissance of my life
that most beautiful name, Bangladesh,
was cried out by beggars for alms.
Biafra, Bangladesh—beyond these
what poetries?

Peasants were slaughtered, refugees ran
in the Renaissance of my life.
I ran from Blake to Marx to Buddha to
the Renaissance of my life.

the blacks penned, starved, tortured under apartheid,
in the Renaissance of my life,
the Moratoriums clamped between police lines and horses;
the tanks rammed back a people along the streets.

In the Renaissance of my life
the cries of the damned crowded my ears,
the curses of the damned poisoned my mouth,
the arms of the damned demolished my verse,
the guilt of two generations hit like the plague
and boarded up the town
in the Renaissance of my life.

Renton de Alwis

To Mona Lisa

I think you are ugly, selfish and too fat.
Why you are a luminary,
    I never could understand.
The rest of the world must be crazy.

Did you ever give yourself totally
    to your man, Mona Lisa?
Did you love him selflessly?
You couldn't. . . .

You wanted the whole world to
    love and adore you. . . .
You would not otherwise have let
    Da Vinci prostitute you to mankind.

I see no beauty in you,
    only an obsession, you are too straight, artificial.
The way you rest your hands on each other,
    so calculatingly,
Your nose is too fine. . . .
You have no heart,
    only a set of lumpy breasts,
    to cover up the hollowness inside. . . .
You clothe yourself to hide all this,
    and took so much space on the canvas.

The critics and others blind,
    had got me to love you for so many years. . . .
throughout my youth,
    until I saw, for myself,
the real YOU.

Reggie Chrysostom

The Unlatched Gate

She told me she had reached the unlatched gate
Hurrying along the darkened tree-lined lane,
   A little flurried, breathless though not late
In time for night before the edge of pain. . . .
   April's trace was still about her face,
About herself an unspoilt note of grace,
   And in unfolding for me all her past
A vague, though not incurious, spell she cast. . . .
   There was no sign of sob, nor catch in voice,
Nor did she carp at what she could not cure,
   She simply said she had no other choice
To gain ingress and latch the gate secure. . . .
   I met her in that cottage once again
While rain tattooed her tale upon the pane. . . .

Jean Arasanayagam

A Country at War

Why pretend that things have not changed
when they have, planting flowers and exotics
in pretty gardens, the magnolias in full bloom
golden carp in pools to make poems with—
excavate the lawns and you'll find weeds
springing out of skulls and the birds in the trees
that sang at dawn grasp the light
with taloned claws dragging nets and setting
snares over the sun; now darkness covers the land.

Our emotions are no longer important
whom we love or loved once or are likely
to love, all these are inconsequentials
our grand passions turned out to be
romantic malingering merely and the agony
of non-requital nothing so painful
as this new feeling, we love with the deepest
passion those who belong wholly to death,
dispense with partings and the obsequies,
why mock the sacrifice, make it cheap
with the false trappings of mourning,
it is what they wished, to part with life
to squander breath, minions of mortality.

Language too must change as we do,
become common, our parley is with the
assassin and the so-called criminals,
we rub shoulders with them in the street
listen carefully to the argot of their speech
if we are to understand at all

why the young now carry arms, make
even defeat a stance that is heroic
shake hands too, laugh, banter
with the death dealers see them as human
even with guilt, utter under our breath
'Father forgive them for they know not what they do,'
others take these picnics seriously
laughter no longer joy-making
your smile could be your death
end up vomiting blood from the kicks
and blows as the ruptured spleen splits and bursts.

We shuffle a deck of cards
spell out new words from their symbols
—the ammunition of our defence—
we are desperate but calm,
a priest prays, actors go on stage
we prepare for journeys and plan futures,
mornings we wake up hopeful, interpret
with sybillic fervour our dreams,
there's a smell of fresh bread baking
from the wood-fire ovens, the smoke
here is not from the incinerators and
at night the rich fireflies shimmer above
the dark hedge, yet we read alarm
in every cry of every insect
and when we sleep we find night dangerous,
the dream turns out to be real
you jostle shoulders with them all
in the crowded cells and touch a shaking
shoulder before the next encounter—the
The *dansant** of death and torture.

This time the explosions did not go off
for the nonce things still stand intact
but it's only a matter of time, the foundation's
wired, perhaps tomorrow the edifice comes down.

---

* (French) tea with dancing

And what of the little tailor and his wife
living in the shanty below the bridge,
they had better sew themselves new skins
or take to cutting shrouds.

Reggie Siriwardena

Waiting for the Soldier

'I hope you'll find a more companionable person to play chess with than a computer.'

—*Nirmala Salgado, in a letter*

After the Roman army took Syracuse,
a soldier, in the midst of the looting and raping,
stopped when he saw a Greek bent over
figures inscribed in the sand. Gaping,

the Roman watched his strange absorption
in that magic of lines and circles. He
(not looking up at the soldier) said, "Move!
With your shadow there it's hard to see!"

The soldier hit him on the head, and so
Archimedes died. If, then, today
I turn more and more to this ordered world
of sixty-four squares, to the mimic play

of forces in a field where nobody bleeds;
where in the intervals of the game my silent friend
won't annoy me by spouting racist drivel
or Marxist simplicities; if the chief end

of life at present seems to be to find
an infallible answer to the French Defence
(my opponent's favourite opening), don't say
I am escaping. In a world without sense

one must look for meaning wherever one
can find it—if only, perhaps, for a day
or two. I know the Roman soldier—
in one shape or another—is on the way.

Reggie Siriwardena

Report from the Front

The subversives had come out, secretly, silently,
after their long waiting underground.
Already, they'd made their first destructive
strike in the dark, before I found

the tell-tale mark in the corner
between two walls—a long, brown
streak, which gave the show away.
Sure enough, in a bookcase, down

under the bottom row, I uncovered
a swarming mass of infiltrators. A spray
gun spat 'chus-chus', and
several hundreds of wreckers lay

dead. I counted my losses—Steiner
('After Babel') partly gone; still,
no serious damage. My sister, however,
(a seasoned general) warned, 'You will

have to be vigilant.' A day passed,
two; on the third, they struck again;
were repulsed; this time they got
a couple of volumes of Mark Twain.

The war goes on. No negotiations
are possible. Of course, I'd like to howl
from the housetops, 'Culture, civilization
threatened! Anarchy! Murder most foul!'

'But the small voice of a termite whispers:
'Comrades, there's a bloated capitalist who keeps
shelves full of food for himself, while we
starve. Come, let's get it while he sleeps!'

Part II

Writing in Sinhalese

Ediriwira Sarachchandra

Of a Queen and a Courtesan

I

Never before, in all his fifteen years of experience in the theatre, had Virasena found himself in such a quandary. Already it was nearly six weeks since he began his new production, but he had not even succeeded in finding a suitable cast. Even in the early days when young men and women of the middle class needed some persuasion before they consented to go on stage, he had never lacked suitable men and women to fit into his roles, and people often remarked how lucky he was in this respect. He had wondered silently whether it should all be attributed to luck, and whether some part of the credit should not come to him for his ability to make an actor out of almost anybody. Or to say the least, could it not be that he was able to spot out, in a kind of instinctive way, the potential that a person possessed, and to envisage the kind of role he would fit into most appropriately? In later years, he had actually come to believe, secretly, that he did possess such an ability, and that it could not be just luck that his performers, although amateurs who had received no previous training, were able to rise up almost to professional standards. This gave him a certain self-confidence which he had not possessed before, for he was able to look back and survey his achievement, measuring it against that of others in the field. The feeling grew within him that not one of them had succeeded so far in bringing on to the stage something that left the audience with quite the same sense of satisfaction and completeness they experienced when seeing a production of his. And whenever he went to see a production of any of the 'lesser' people in the field, his feeling found confirmation within him, for there seemed to be something always lacking, something that did not quite click. He knew that was how the audience felt, too, although it was seldom that they gave expression to their feelings. Once, when he had been lying low for a while without producing anything, he had met a person he didn't know too well who had asked him, 'Why don't you give us another play, Mr Virasena? We have been waiting long.' And he had replied, 'Well, there is no dearth of plays, is there?' At which his interlocutor had said, 'But we want something by you. It doesn't look as if any of the others can deliver the goods.' Virasena had been embarrassed at this remark, but it had left him with a feeling of secret satisfaction.

In the situation in which he found himself now, Virasena almost felt his self-confidence waning, and he began to entertain serious doubts about himself. Could it not be that, after all, it was nothing but luck that had helped him up till now, and that this luck had begun to desert him? Otherwise, how was it that he was not making any progress in the last several weeks? Rehearsals had now become a drudgery to him, and he did nothing but just sit and watch, hoping that someone among his players would show but the slightest spark of creativeness, something that he could work on, something that would stimulate him to arrive at some creative conception of the play he was producing. He knew, that was what was lacking: he was unable to work on the play creatively. That was why the whole thing had become such a drudgery to him, and why he felt so completely depressed at rehearsals. Is it that he had not first sat down and thought out everything before he began to work with the cast? But that was not his usual method. He was never used to working with a preconceived idea of what the final shape of his production was to be like. He always began with a hazy notion of what he was aiming at, and the thing grew gradually, helped along by spurts of inspiration that came to him in the course of the rehearsals. It was only towards the end that he himself gained a clear conception of what the final product was going to be like. Only then would he begin to work consciously and deliberately, toning down here and exaggerating there, filling gaps, adding a few things and erasing others according to his sense of balance and proportion, like a painter who had got the rough outline of his picture and was filling in the details.

But things were not working out the same way this time. And he knew the reason. He wanted the players to provide the initial conditions which would bring out the inspiration within him, but this time they were not doing it. In a sense he could not blame them; they did everything he asked them to do, and very faithfully, too. But reciprocally, they did nothing on their own, whether good or bad. They were only receiving, but giving nothing in return. 'Let them even do something wrong,' he told himself, 'so that I could correct them, so that my reaction against it might give me some positive ideas.' As he looked back and analysed how he had worked before, he realized how that had been his method. It was the first time that he was beginning to be consciously aware of it. And in order to reassure himself that something was not wrong with him, that he had not, perchance, exhausted his creative powers, he looked back upon himself and his work more and more. Actually he began to formulate for himself certain theories about acting and producing, and about the creative impulse in general. The creative impulse of the actor and the creative impulse of the director must mutually interact, and out of this interaction would emerge the final synthesis which was the finished play on the stage. But in this instance one of the two elements needed for the interaction was absent, namely the creative impulse of the actor, and hence the process was not taking place.

Should he try to alter the cast? At the moment this seemed to be the only alternative to giving up the production entirely. But as he ran his mind through each member of the cast in turn, there was no one he could for certain say was not suitable for the role he had been cast in. They all seemed to possess the potentiality, and he felt sure that given time they would all give a fair account of themselves. When the time came to teach them the songs and the dance movements, it was just possible that some interchange of parts would be necessary. But in general he felt confident about all of them. And as the faces of each of them came to his mind in turn, his heart melted for all of them, he knew he loved them all. How could he tell anyone of them that he was not suitable or that he must be tried in another role or that he should be cast away completely? They were all so sincere and attached to their parts and enjoyed so much doing them.

If he had any doubts at all it was about the two women in the cast. He had the greatest difficulty in casting the female roles, one of which was that of a queen and the other that of a royal courtesan. He had to reject two or three before making his final decision, but his choice was limited, because, even these days, not many middle-class parents would like their daughters going on stage. This was something to be expected, however, and when he finally settled on two of the girls, he felt he could make do with them. It is true they did not possess the looks that would have been desirable for roles such as theirs, but what could he do but choose from among those who presented themselves? The girl he had cast as queen was ugly by any standards, he told himself. But as far as the queen's role was concerned, he told himself, it did not matter. The queen did not have to be pretty, her character was ugly, and why shouldn't her appearance be in keeping with it? And she seemed to have what is called a stage personality, her features were big and her singing voice was tolerable. She spoke in a kind of monotone, but he thought she would improve as she began to understand the import of the words better. The girl he had chosen for the courtesan was by no means pretty, either, but as he kept on surveying her, taking in every single feature of her face, watching her every movement and running his eye along every single curve of her body, he felt convinced that apart from some awkwardness she displayed because she was not used to the stage, she could not be regarded as exactly ugly. In fact, with the help of clever make-up, he felt she could be made to look as attractive as a royal courtesan was expected to look. There were moments, however, when he was assailed by doubts and thought about how much it would have added to the play if the courtesan's role was performed by a girl who was at least conventionally beautiful, with lighter skin and a sharp nose and long eyes that would cast coquettish sidelong glances like the women in the Sigiriya frescoes. But again he reassured himself by saying, 'How do I know what people's tastes actually are? I would be the last person to call this girl beautiful, but you never know how audiences would react.' He recalled how, in an earlier production of his, he had chosen for the main female role a girl whom one wouldn't care to look at twice, but who had a good singing voice and was interpreting her character well. And he was surprised when, after the first performance, some of his friends went into ecstasies over her, saying that she was extremely attractive and resembled one of the dark beauties of Ajanta. Such is the spell that the magic world of the stage can cast on an audience.

Virasena was, therefore, unable to understand what was wrong.

No doubt, something was lacking. He could not detect that spark which would brighten up the whole performance; even if it didn't brigthen up the rehearsals, it could spark on opening night. There wasn't also that two-way communication between him and the actors: they gave him nothing that he could mould into something beautiful and hand back to them. The whole performance, therefore, lacked the creative touches of his earlier productions, those sparks of originality which he knew were the things that added up to give the entire production the satisfying quality that people talked of.

The best thing, thought Virasena at last, would be to see how another person would react to the performance in its present shape. His wife, Samanmali, had asked him once or twice how rehearsals were going, and he had said he was not too pleased. At that time he did not want to ask her to come and watch a rehearsal, because he feared she might say things that would only add to the discouragement he himself felt. Now, perhaps, he might ask her to come and make her comments. He could also ask Mahanama, whose judgment as a critic he respected. There were a few others, too, who were experienced playgoers, whose reactions he might watch, although he might not be able to accept their criticisms. Normally he would not have invited any of these people so early, but would have reserved them for a dress-rehearsal audience had he not found himself at this impasse.

After the rehearsal he sipped beer with Mahanama and discussed the play late into the night. The rest had offered no comments, and Virasena knew that their silence could have only one meaning. Mahanama's opinion, which Samanmali, too, heartily endorsed, was that the female roles would have to be recast. The queen was very unsatisfactory, they both thought, and he ought to find a better-looking girl for the courtesan.

'Do you want me to make Sinhalese girls look more beautiful than they really are?' asked Virasena, taking refuge in his usual cynicism.

'It is not only a question of looks,' said Mahanama. 'Take the queen. Whether you want to make her look ugly or beautiful, what's the point? She can't act for the life of her. After all, her part is pivotal in the play and I think that's what's wrong with the whole thing.'

Virasena tried not to be offended by his friend's forthrightness, reasoning with himself that, after all, what he had asked for was frank criticism. But the result was that he became perverse and more determined to carry on with the cast he had. It was almost a challenge to him, and he thought he ought to prove, as in his previous productions, that he could make an actor out of almost any human being.

And so things went on. Virasena alternated between moods of optimism and moods of depression, and in the meantime, the suggestion that what was wrong with the play was the casting of the queen, began, gradually, to appear to him to be correct. There were still a few occasions when the girl did her bit convincingly, and he felt that the critics were wrong, but then, he argued, after all it is the reactions of the audience that matter and not his personal feelings. And both Mahanama as well as Samanmali were certainly representative members of the audience. But there was nothing he could do but continue.

A few weeks later Virasena received a letter signed by an unknown person. It was the kind of letter he often received, and which he had recently begun to relegate to the waste-paper basket. They all said the same thing: 'Please give me an opportunity to take part in one of your plays. I have a great desire to act and feel that I have talent. . . . ' In the beginning he used to write back and summon them to auditions, or at least to an interview so that he could see what they looked like. But in recent days he had stopped replying. Most of them were young men and women who had left school after taking their Senior Certificates, or after having failed their examinations a number of times, and who thought they might try their hand at acting. He did not know for what reason they wanted to go on stage, because the stage did not offer them a career. Perhaps their young hearts were fired with enthusiasm after seeing a play or two done in the school hall of their little home-towns. They could not have seen very much, in any case, because these school halls were not made to perform the functions of a theater: no one who gets a seat behind the first five or six rows could see anything but the heads of the actors. Nor could they have heard much either, except a song or two, perhaps. But the magic of the theatre had gripped them, and they wanted to become actors and actresses. When Virasena invited and tested them he found that they possessed nothing but their enthusiasm. He felt sorry for them, but he had to tell them the truth and send them away. These young people from the village wanted, perhaps, to play their part in the new awakening in the arts, but they had not had the opportunity to receive the necessary training. And he couldn't give them that. After all, he was an amateur play director himself, and could only work with people who had already got a training of some sort, even in the allied arts of music and dancing if not in dramatic art proper.

After a time he felt it was futile even to reply to the letters he received from such young enthusiasts, and began laughing at himself that he had ever taken them seriously. Perhaps the romanticism contained in Gray's lines:

Full many a gem of purest ray serene
The dark unfathomed caves of ocean bear

had impelled him earlier, and he had expected to make some startling discovery by exploring these unknown sources. But now, he told himself, he was hardened to facts and knew that such miracles did not happen in ordinary life, that actors could only emerge out of training or out of a live dramatic tradition, and not just from nowhere.

His first impulse was to throw away this letter too, straight into the waste-paper basket, but something suddenly restrained him, and instead, he left it on his table among his other correspondence. Perhaps some faint hope arose within him when he read the letter. It said, 'I can sing and dance, but have not, so far, taken part in any play.' Perhaps the subconscious thought that even an extra singer might be a useful addition to the chorus might have influenced his decision not to throw away the letter. Now, in his desperation, he resolved to clutch at this last straw. He reminded himself, however, that he should not pin too many hopes on it. He wrote asking the applicant to come and see him.

For almost a week there was no response to his letter, and he dropped the matter and continued with his rehearsals, reconciled, more or less, to the players he had. He felt they were improving gradually, and was beginning to have more confidence in them. 'After all, one cannot tell how they will turn out to be in the presence of an audience,' he told himself. It had happened to him more than once, that an actor whom he had given up as hopeless and had left to fend for himself as best he could, suddenly flowered on the first night and even carried the play along with him.

Then, one afternoon, he answered a feeble knock on the door to see, standing on the step, a slip of a girl attired in a frock of what seemed to him to be of cheap material, looking up at him with a broad smile as if expecting him to recognize her and greet her arrival like that of a long lost friend. Her face was wan and her lips somewhat withered, but there was something about her. He wondered what it was, and decided it must be her eyes which were unusually long and placed slantwise on her face, not with the upward slant of Mongolian eyes, but with the outer corners inclining down in the direction of her ears. He looked her up and down and saw that her legs were thin and unshapely for her body, which, though small, was well grown. His eyes rested for a moment on her full, young bosom, for it was the most conspicuous element in her figure, and just then she burst out into a shy chuckle, as if she had read his mind, and showed him an envelope that had been addressed in handwriting that he recognised to be his own.

He quickly pulled himself together, feeling somewhat ashamed of himself, and remembering, at the same time, the letter he had written a few days back. He was somewhat annoyed that the girl should have chosen such a time at which to visit him, because he was just getting ready to have a short rest in bed before going to evening rehearsals. However, she held the letter before him as if in answer to his charge, and he recalled that he hadn't given her an appointment. The best thing, he thought, would be to attend to her at once and send her away. It wouldn't take more than ten minutes at the most, and then he could lie down for at least half an hour.

He showed her to his study and she walked in, after first leaving her slippers at the door. He was charmed by this act of hers. 'How courteous these village people are,' he thought. 'They are sure of themselves, and are not torn between two cultures, like the people I have to deal with.' He pointed to the mat on which lay his *tamboura**, and sat down after her.

'Sing something. Any song you know,' he said, getting down to business at once, and touching the strings of his *tamboura*. She

---

* stringed intrument, the function of which is similar to that of the drone in a bagpipe

began without hesitation, and he was glad to find that her pitch was correct. It was so seldom that his singers were able to get at the correct pitch by listening to the *sruti** of the *tamboura*; he had often to play for them the first note of the song. She was sure of her notes and her *tala***as well, but he thought her voice was harsh and grating. It was not necessary to test her too long. He concluded that she would certainly be useful in the play, perhaps to add volume to the weak voices of the chorus. But, as he had suspected, she could not be substituted in any of the female parts; she was too small-made to be suitable for the queen, and she was not good-looking enough to be cast in the role of courtesan. So he sent her away, telling her that if she liked she might come to the rehearsals and learn the songs because she might be able to join the chorus.

'You see, I have already cast the play,' he explained to her with a smile, 'I will keep you in mind when I am doing something else.'

Samanmali was seated in the veranda and saw the girl going out. Virasena knew that she had probably listened to her singing as well.

'What do you think of her?' he asked her after the girl had left.

'I think she is quite smart,' she replied. 'Almost pretty, I might say.'

Virasena was amazed at his wife's comments. 'What? Pretty, did you say? Are you crazy?'

'Well, that's how I felt at first glance. What an unusual pair of eyes she has.'

'Yes, that's true about her eyes,' said Virasena, wondering how his wife had been able to observe the girl so carefully. 'But her figure is unshapely. Look at her legs, how thin they are.'

Samanmali was silent. She either resented his comments or failed to understand them, and Virasena began to re-examine his own opinion. Couldn't it be that his judgment was much too influenced by western notions of female beauty? Didn't the ancient Indian poets describe their ideal women as having thin calves enfeebled by the weight of their breasts and hips?

He was somewhat surprised when he found that the girl was actually present at the evening rehearsal. When he sent her

---

* dominant pitch; **time measure

away, he thought she would be so disappointed that she would never come again, and he didn't mind it. He could recall instances of several young people who came forward to take part in his plays, and showed they could sing a song or two that they had picked up from the radio, but who couldn't tackle more difficult music.

'This is Gunavati,' he said introducing her to the rest of the cast, and hastened to add, 'I have brought her so that she could take part in the chorus.' He did not want the female players to feel that he had intended her to be a substitute for any one of them. It was true that he had often threatened to remove them if they didn't improve, but they seemed to be doing their best. This was a stage at which they needed words of encouragement and not any more threats.

When Virasena directed a play, he trained the singers himself. In the early days it was a pleasant business teaching the actors the songs, but recently he found that his musical memory was failing him and that he often couldn't remember the melodies. And since the music of most of the plays was not in notation, he was finding it more and more difficult to look after this part of the production without the assistance of a musician. But since musicians were not always available, he began to make use of a tape-recorder after having first got the melodies recorded. He now found Gunavati to be a great asset, because she had an astoundingly quick and accurate musical memory and could reproduce a melody almost on hearing it for the first time. Hardly had a week passed when she had mastered all the music of the play, whereas the actors who had to sing them actually were still making mistakes. Whenever they sang a false note or faltered in their timing he would make a sign to Gunavati and she would sing the song correctly, and he didn't have to refer to the recorded version at all. Actually he hadn't, so far, paid much attention to the singing, and now he realized, after Gunavati began to sing the songs, how imperfectly his actors were rendering them. It often happened that, throughout a rehearsal, Gunavati sang most of the songs, because it transpired that hardly anybody was singing them perfectly.

After this had gone on for some time, Virasena told them, 'Look, we must get on with the play. We cannot make use of rehearsal time for learning songs. I would suggest that each of you arrange to meet Gunavati privately and brush up your songs.'

A fortnight later they were making the same mistakes, and he became impatient with them. Even the chief male actor who played the king's role was singing false notes.

'Subasinghe, I am sure you haven't practised your songs with Gunavati,' he told him. 'Will you do so without much delay?'

Subasinghe said nothing. He seemed displeased and turned a sour face. Virasena wondered why, and looked hard at the man. He was about thirty-five and somewhat elderly in appearance. Did he resent being asked to learn from a mere slip of a girl? If so, it was a stupid attitude and he must correct it.

The female players, too, had not improved in the intervening time when he expected that they would have been practising with Gunavati.

'Didn't Gunavati correct your mistakes?' he asked Sila who played the queen. 'You are singing the same wrong notes over and over again, and at this rate you will never be able to sing the right tune.' She stood looking down and did not reply.

Virasena questioned Ramya, the courtesan. 'You need to improve your singing too. Did you fix up with Gunavati to teach you?'

A titter passed around, particularly among the girls who formed the chorus. But there was no reply from anyone. He looked from face to face and they were all blank. Gunavati sat silently in a corner, separated from the rest.

'Haven't you been helping them?' he asked her. She simply moved her head in denial.

Virasena was exasperated. What could be at the bottom of all this? Did his players fear competition from Gunavati? He had explained to them that she was only going to be an addition to the chorus. They ought to welcome an opportunity to perfect themselves in their singing. Or could it be that Gunavati herself was showing reluctance to teach them, in the hope that she could step into the shoes of one of them?

'I am going to stop all rehearsals until you learn the songs. Let Gunavati meet you here. When you are perfect, come and inform me,' he said and walked out of the room.

Subasinghe followed him up to the car. He was not only chief actor in the play, but stage manager, secretary of the dramatic club, and everything else as well. It was he who had invited Virasena to produce a play for them, and now he looked very concerned.

'You can begin practising right now,' Virasena told him as he stepped into the car. 'It is still quite early in the evening. And you can come and tell me how things are going.'

Samanmali saw her husband returning early from rehearsals, and suspected that something must have gone wrong.

'What happened? Did somebody keep away?' she asked.

'No. They are fairly regular in their attendance. But they don't know their songs yet. And they don't want to learn either.'

'What do you mean they don't want to learn?'

'Well, I asked them to learn their songs from Gunavati because she knows them so well already. But apparently they don't like her, or she doesn't like them. . . . I don't know which is which.'

'If I were you I would put Gunavati in the role of queen and be done with it. Then you won't have any anxiety on account of the singing.'

'Gunavati as queen?' asked Virasena in surprise. 'Surely that is unthinkable. A queen must look at least dignified. She must have size.'

'What's wrong with Gunavati? When I saw her for the first time I thought she would be ideal to play the queen. And why do you say she is not dignified? When you put her in a costume she will have all the dignity you need.'

Virasena felt so vexed that he thought it best not to continue the argument lest he lose control of himself and say something nasty. With regard to females he always found his wife's judgment very strange and quite in contrast to his. Many times he wanted to tell her that matters relating to female beauty had better be left to the judgment of males. But he felt it was useless winning an ideological victory with her. As a practical man of the theatre it was more important for him to know how people felt, and the question of whether they were right or wrong was irrelevant.

Later in the evening Mahanama strolled in. 'I went to the theatre but heard you had cancelled the practice and gone home early,' he said.

'I wish you had come home earlier. I had a problem which you could have helped me tackle.'

Virasena went on to explain to his friend the strange behaviour of the cast and its attitude towards Gunavati.

Mahanama smiled knowingly. 'I can tell you all about it,' he said, 'I met Subasinghe just now and also talked to some of the others.'

Mahanama had an uncanny way of getting behind-the-scenes information. He knew most of the members of the cast personally because, as a critic, and a man generally interested in theatre, he had cultivated their acquaintance—going backstage after a performance and talking to them, commenting on their acting, and even getting to know their personal problems. He was their confidant, because they had closer access to him, whereas Virasena was a person they respected from a distance.

'Why do they resent her? Are they afraid that I will get rid of one of them and put her in?'

'Actually it is a kind of social prejudice, as I gather. They don't seem to like someone from outside their social class joining them in their activities.'

'It is really that, is it?' said Virasena, trying not to be surprised. 'I had a suspicion but couldn't believe it was possible. How did you know? They couldn't have told you such a thing directly.'

'Of course, they didn't tell me directly. But I learned everything from Somalatha, the girl in the chorus who lives near my place. I have been hearing things for some time now, and wanted to come and talk to you when I got a chance. You won't believe it, but they don't even offer her a cup of tea at rehearsals. There are things you wouldn't notice yourself. And she has to walk back alone all the way to Enderamulla. There are three of them living close to that village but they avoid going with her. She has been practically ostracized by them.'

Virasena felt very sorry for Gunavati, and at the same time his heart filled with contempt for the others. 'I always knew that these middle-class fellows were hypocrites and that they had far too many inhibitions to make them suited to the theatre. But I didn't realize they were so snobbish.'

'Oh, I suppose they will adjust their attitudes and accept her as time goes.'

'They will have to accept her, I am afraid, if they want to continue in my play,' said Virasena, and there was a veiled threat in his tone. 'They must acknowledge talent wherever they see it, if they want to be artists at all.'

II

It was partly to teach his cast a lesson in cooperation, and partly to give Gunavati the opportunity she deserved so well, that Virasena finally decided to cast her in the queen's role. He thought it best to talk straight to everybody and explain why he was forced to do it. It might help to lessen their antagonism to Gunavati if they were made to realize that the play could not go on without her. To soften the effect of his move he told them how every single person in a play was important and that it was merely that some people fitted certain roles better than others. Everybody had to think of the success of the play, and make their individual contribution, however small, with this goal in view. Not that he believed every word he said, but some sort of explanation was necessary before making such a great change. He hated making speeches and spouting homilies, and hoped it was the last time he would have to perform such an unpleasant task.

As he watched this wisp of a creature practising her part with the rest, he couldn't yet make himself believe that she was fitted to play the role of a queen, and told himself several times that his wife must be wrong. The best he could hope for was that she would make up for her physical inadequacies with her powerful voice. He could not imagine how a costume could transform her to that extent, and confer on her a regal dignity which was as far removed from her appearance in normal life as the earth is from the sky. As time went on he found that she had other assets as well besides her voice. She intoned her words correctly and conducted herself with poise on the stage. There was also rhythm and movement in her frail body, and he felt he could handle these assets so as to give her something of the personality she otherwise lacked.

What was most remarkable, however, was that she brought into the rehearsals that mysterious dynamic quality which he had been looking for all the while but had not found. As soon as she had learned her words, the play began moving in a way it had not moved before. The actors responded and improved remarkably within a matter of weeks. And Virasena discovered, to his great joy, that the springs of creativity within him had not been exhausted after all. He was now inspired, and was able to give his production those masterly touches that had distinguished his earlier works. His task had now ceased to be the drudgery that it had been before. On the other hand, it was giving him the greatest pleasure. He was seeing his creation come to life before his eyes.

Mahanama was pleased, and so was Samanmali. She said, pointing to Gunavati with obvious pride, almost appropriating the entire credit to herself, 'Look at the way she walks. Look at the angle of her head. And the commanding tone of her voice. When she sings, how it rises and falls in waves, filling the hall with melody.'

The frictions between Gunavati and the rest of the cast seemed to have been smoothed out, and they all appeared to be treating her like one of them. Sila took her place in the chorus without complaint. The girls joined with Gunavati and they walked together to the rehearsals and back, leaving Gunavati by her house at Enderamulla. And there was a friendly atmosphere during the practices. Virasena made it a special point to see that she was served tea, and told his wife, too, to keep an eye on her. He began to wonder, after a while, whether Mahanama was exaggerating, or had got some wrong information about Gunavati being discriminated against, because things went on very well.

Then one *poya* morning, Gunavati came unexpectedly to the house, and sobbing before Virasena and his wife, said she wanted to quit the play.

'Why, what is it all about?' asked Virasena. He was planning to get the constumes designed and fix a date for the opening, and was naturally perturbed.

Gunavati had a long story to tell them.

'It has gone on for a long time,' she said, 'and on many occasions I wanted to drop out but didn't because of you.'

'Don't think of dropping out now,' said Virasena. 'I will have to give up doing the play if you drop out. Tell us what your troubles are, and we will try to do something about it.'

'There's nothing you can do. They just don't want me. You ought to find somebody else whom they will accept. Perhaps they think I am a poor village girl who should not be in their company.'

'What made you feel so?'

'There's nothing they don't do to make me feel so. They've been calling me names. They make remarks whenever I pass by their houses. I didn't mind that. But yesterday, when I was going to the rehearsals, Subasinghe's wife called me into the house. I was with some of the other girls, and we all went in. Then she began to abuse me, calling me a prostitute. She pulled me by the hair and slapped me in the face.'

Virasena was stunned with amazement, and Samanmali turned her fury on him. 'What a pack of idiots you have chosen to do a play with,' she snapped. 'And you put this innocent girl into their midst.'

'This sort of thing has never happened before in my experience,' said Virasena apologetically.

'You must get rid of Subasinghe immediately,' said Samanmali.

'I don't think he is to blame,' pleaded Gunavati. 'He has been quite nice to me recently, although he was somewhat distant in the beginning. I think his wife is a jealous sort of woman.'

'If his wife is jealous, he ought not to take part in plays with women in the cast.'

'I think she is a very ignorant woman, who doesn't know what play-acting is. In the beginning I was only amused by her; she did such crazy things. She has about half-a-dozen children, and when I pass by her house, she used to call them out and pointing to me say, "Children, there goes your father's queen. Take a good look at her." '

'What were the other girls doing in the meantime, when this was happening to you?' asked Samanmali, who in spite of her anger, couldn't suppress a smile.

'They did nothing. They just looked on, enjoying the fun.'

'You mean they did not even protest that the woman was making unfair accusations? They did not try to stop her beating you?' asked Virasena.

'No, they didn't. That's just the point!' Samanmali's tone was bitter and sarcastic. 'That's just the point! They all stood by and enjoyed what was happening. They would have done the same thing to Gunavati themselves if they had half the chance. They all hate her. They will kill her some day.'

She worked herself up to a frenzy with every new sentence. Virasena recalled that when he first asked Gunavati to come to the rehearsals, a faint doubt had crossed his mind as to how the others might take it. But he had asked himself, in what way was she different from the rest? They would come to know, of course, that she lived in a little hut in the village of Enderamulla, and not in one of the middle-class houses on the outskirts where most of the others lived. But would they resent associations with her on those grounds? The village of Enderamulla, he had been told, did not enjoy a very high reputation, but Gunavati was a decent girl, and would they count that against her? It is true she wore a frock, but not all the others came all the time in a saree. Some of them came to the rehearsals quite often attired in frocks. Perhaps their frocks were a little more fashionable in style, and Gunavati's were of cheaper material. Once or twice he had wanted to suggest to his wife to buy some dress material for Gunavati and make for her a couple of frock which would resemble those worn by the others. But he felt squeamish to talk of such matters, and wondered whether he was exaggerating things in his own mind. He didn't, for a moment, expect to encounter social prejudice in such crude shape as this, or imagine that the rest of them would all get together and indulge in the systematic persecution of a newcomer merely on the ground that she did not belong to their class. Now he felt himself responsible for putting Gunavati in such an embarrassing situation. He told himself that he should have been more realistic, that he should have anticipated that something like this was going to happen. Now, it was his duty to save her from the evil he had exposed her to.

'I am prepared to drop this entirely and begin later with a new cast who will be more friendly to you,' he said.

'No, don't do that. Don't drop the play because of me. Besides, you have taken all the trouble to train these people. The better thing will be for me to drop out, and you can find someone else to do my part.'

'That's impossible. I won't do it in any case. That will be only encouraging this kind of pettiness. Anyway, you stop worrying. I will talk to them this evening. For the present you stay away from the rehearsals.'

They talked the matter over further after Gunavati had left.

'I don't think you ought to drop the play entirely,' said Samanmali who was beginning to cool off. 'That will be like punishing Gunavati, because you will deprive her of this chance. You ought to do something to make the fellows realize their own folly.'

Virasena was glad that his wife encouraged the idea of continuing with the play, because, in spite of the threats he made, he knew he would be sorry if he had to drop it entirely.

'Let's inquire into the whole incident and find out who the culprits are,' he said. 'I can't believe that all of them share these prejudices. After all, don't they profess to be socialists, most of them?'

With this last question he looked at Samanmali with a sour smile.

That evening he spoke to the cast in solemn tones.

'Strange things have been happening, and I have remained so far unaware of them. Now matters have come to a head, and we can't continue with the play, I am afraid. You know what I am referring to. It is most unfortunate that such a thing should have taken place. The result of it all is that Gunavati refuses to come any more. And I can't ask her to come, either. Actually if I had guessed that there would be so much hostility to her, I wouldn't have asked her to come in the first instance. I am sure you all want to do the play. We have spent so much of our time and energies on it that it would be a pity to drop it now. But I leave it to you to find someone else who can play the part of the queen. I found somebody for you, but you don't like her. Now it is your turn to look for someone. Will you find someone, and soon?'

They all remained with their eyes downcast, looking thoroughly dejected and penitent. No one spoke a word, and after a while Virasena said, 'That is all I have to tell you now. Apparently you can't think of anybody offhand. I leave it to you to look for someone and let me know.'

This said, he walked away.

There was a lull for a few days, and nobody came to see Virasena. He began to get curious as to what was happening. The suspicion that his cast might have decided to abandon the play made him feel uneasy. He was actually beginning to miss the rehearsals and found the evenings dull, and with all the heartburn that the production gave him, he still felt he would like it to go on.

He thought Mahanama might have some information and went to see him.

'Yes, I heard about it all,' said Mahanama, with a promising smile on his face. 'Subasinghe came to me, and so did some of the others. They are very hurt about what you did. I wonder if you haven't been rather hasty.'

'Hasty, you say? I am surprised to hear you say so. I am sure you don't know the other side of the story.'

'Well, Vire, you know only one side yourself.'

'And that's the only side worth knowing.'

'I am not at all sure. Do you know what they say? They feel you are too partial to this girl, and that she carries tales to you, so that you get a distorted view of things.'

'That's nonsense. She didn't tell me anything till this nasty incident happened. Ask Samanmali if you don't believe me.'

'I think you ought to be more realistic in your approach. When you bring a raw girl from the village and put her among more sophisticated actors, there is bound to be a clash. Particularly when she offers competition to the others.'

'This has nothing to do with sophistication. It is nothing but middle-class snobbishness and prudery. I am surprised to find you condoning that kind of thing.'

'I am not condoning it. But you mustn't attach too much importance to such things. You shouldn't forget that Gunavati has a tendency to impose herself on the others. She is almost aggressive, I must say. I wonder if she doesn't exploit your wholesale partiality to her. Naturally the others won't like it.'

'She has to put up a fight, doesn't she, if she wants to find a place in the sun? After all, she comes from a hard world, and she has to be tough to survive in it.'

'I think she is tough enough to fight the battle by herself. Your interference doesn't seem to help her very much.'

'Do you think I should allow her to be insulted by the ignorant wives of these chaps, and her name to be tarnished? She is a young girl. How will it affect her future? She has a brilliant career before her as an artist. Should she embark on it with such a cloud over her head?'

Virasena felt somewhat ashamed of himself when he saw the smile of amusement on Mahanama's face. He realized he was becoming sentimental.

During the next few days, several deputations of three and four at a time came to see Virasena in his house. They were all full of apologies, and expressed a desire to continue with the play. Subasinghe, too, was with them. He looked thoroughly beaten, and wouldn't utter a word. Perhaps everybody was blaming him for the incident, thought Virasena. He felt very sorry for the man. 'After all, we don't know what personal problems these people have,' he mused. 'They are not professional actors and they have to spend their evenings away from home. Their wives are obliged to stay in, and, naturally, they imagine that dreadful things are happening.'

Three of them came without Subasinghe one day and made direct reference to the incident offering an explanation.

'This is the first time that Subasinghe has taken part in a play, and his wife doesn't understand these things,' they said. 'To add to that, some mischievous tongues have been wagging. They have given her the impression that Gunavati is a girl of loose character, and she got scared when she heard it.'

'This is what it all boils down to, as I have been saying all the time,' butted in Samanmali impatiently. 'They are out to have her blood. They won't give her a chance.'

'You must learn to stand together and not indulge in malicious gossip about one another,' said Virasena. 'Everyone of you must take the responsibility for this, and not blame just one or two.'

'It is up to you to safeguard the reputation of your women and not go about spreading scandals about them.'

'Perhaps you ought to change some of your traditional attitudes towards women if you want to take part in this kind of activity,' added Virasena. 'When you are doing a play, men and women have to move about freely with one another, and this is bound to give rise to gossip. It is not surprising if outsiders talk, but you must not say uncharitable things about your own colleagues. On the contrary, you must defend one another and try to squash the rumours that start outside your own circle.'

Virasena found himself giving them a homily in a manner he had never been wont to, and was surprised to see himself acting in the role of moral adviser. He had never talked on matters of morality, discipline or propriety to the groups with which he had worked previously, always believing that his task was to train actors in their job and not to look after their morals. And he had openly expressed the view that he was not concerned with their morals as long as they observed the discipline necessary for doing their work efficiently. But this time he was impelled in a strange way, and at the end of his homily he felt good.

'You must apologize to Gunavati if you want her to come back,' he said. And since they most readily agreed to do so, he announced that he was prepared to begin rehearsals once more.

III

The play was at last ready and a date for the trial show had been fixed. It had taken Virasena over three months, which was a longer time than he had spent on any production before. No other production before had seen as many vicissitudes—and as strange ones—as this, and he was glad he was able to steer through them successfully and bring the show before the public at last. The members of the cast had now become not only competent players, but as a result of the tensions that had arisen amongst them, and the crises they had experienced, had come to understand one another and him as well. They were united as he had never known a set of players to be, and he felt that strong bonds of affection had grown between each of them on the one hand, and between them all and him on the other.

About two weeks before the scheduled date of the opening performance, however, he heard a bit of news that made him anxious.

'I am told that Gunavati is not too well,' said Samanmali. 'Don't you think you had better take her to a doctor before it is too late?'

'What is it?'

His face showed such concern that Samanmali hastened to reassure him. 'It's nothing serious. I only thought I should tell you in time, because you have only two weeks left. She's had having a boil under her armpit these last several days and has been dancing with great difficulty.'

'I am glad you told me. Let's take her to Doctor Vijevardana at once. He'll give her an injection and it will disappear. Otherwise her parents will take her to an ayurvedic physician and things will get prolonged.'

Doctor Vijevardana, who had been Virasena's family physician for many years, examined Gunavati for about fifteen minutes and made a gesture of apology to Samanamli. When she left the consultation room along with Gunavati, Virasena asked him in an anxious tone. 'Can she take part in my play a fortnight hence?'

The doctor smiled. 'I am afraid she won't be able to, for a long time to come. Anyhow, it depends on the result of some tests which you will have to get done at the General Hospital.'

'Is it anything so serious as all that? I thought she just had a boil under her armpit.'

'She has been having a series of them. And I can see another coming under her left armpit. It's a sure sign of tuberculosis.'

'Tuberculosis? It cannot be. She is slim, but quite wiry. I have never known her to have taken ill these last three months. They were very strenuous, and sometimes we went on rehearsing till late at night.'

'Well, it could be the result of the strain, now that you say so. She is undernourished, as you can see for yourself, and anaemic. Late nights and the strain of practising could have brought it on. In any case she must be treated surgically for the boils, which means she must spend about a week in hospital. After that she must go though some tests, and even if you eliminate T.B. I would suggest that you give her some rest and good food for at least a month before you resume your practices. Otherwise, even if she hasn't T.B. now, she is sure to get it.'

'I don't believe she has T.B., whatever you may say.'

Virasena was in the habit of talking frankly with the doctor who indulged him even when he expressed the common mis-conceptions a layman has about medicine. 'She has never had even a cold these last three months, although she used to go back and forth from rehearsals in the pouring rain.'

Doctor Vijevardana smiled. 'Just look at her,' he said with assurance, 'she is mere skin and bone. And look at her colour. She hasn't an ounce of blood in her. I have seen hundreds of cases like that. They all come from villages where the diet is deficient. They may have rice, but that is not enough.'

Virasena reported the conversation to his wife, but with strict instructions that she should not breathe about it to anybody. 'They ostracized her merely because she didn't belong to their class. What will they do if they hear she has T.B.?' he asked.

But he kept on saying over and over again, half to himself and half for Samanmali to hear: 'It couldn't be. I am not a medical man, but I am sure Vijevardana is wrong. She has a powerful pair of lungs. People with T.B. are not like that.'

Samanmali merely listened. She did not know about such things, but she hoped, fervently, that her husband was right. In a way, she was more worried about Gunavati than even her husband himself. For Virasena it would be a personal defeat if Gunavati couldn't take part in the play. If that happened, what could he tell the cast? He knew the stock platitudes that would come to the forefront. Illness was a thing sent by the gods and it would only prove that they were correct. The girl brought bad luck and evil. She was no good. That is why the play could not be done. She must be got rid of even now. He was not worried about the tuberculosis. Not that he didn't care what happened to the girl, but because he knew that tuberculosis was not the dreaded disease it was some years back. With proper medical attention and good nourishment she could be brought back to normal in a matter of months, and she could become as healthy as any individual. But he would be losing on a point of principle if he had to do the play without her. It was a matter of face-saving more than anything else.

For Samanmali it was different. She shared with the others the traditional fear of the disease, and was greatly concerned for Gunavati. She took milk and eggs and puddings daily to the hospital for her, because she knew what the food given to patients was like, and comforted her by saying that as soon as her boils were cured the play could be performed. On her part, Gunavati believed that some black magic had been practised on her by the others, and Samanmali reassured her, although half-believing in the possibility herself, that it was nothing of the sort, and that it was merely that she had been working too hard. And Virasena was quite happy that his wife bestowed all this care on Gunavati, and that she did not seem to entertain, even remotely, any jealous thoughts. . . .

In about a week Gunavati was discharged from the hospital, and all the tests declared that she had no tuberculosis.

'I know Vijevardana well,' said Virasena with an air of triumph, 'he likes to strike an alarm so that people get warned in time. And anyhow, it's a good thing we got her properly checked up. She was looking somewhat pale and tired towards the end. Now, of course, no one need know that there was even a suspicion of this sort.'

IV

When the play came on the boards at last Virasena felt it was worth all that he had put into it. It was the work of a contemporary playwright who had based it on a Buddhist legend, and was about a queen being jealous of a royal courtesan because she suspected that her husband made love to the courtesan. The queen plots to have the courtesan killed. There were some revisions and final touches which he felt he could put into it at a later date, but he was satisfied with the thing as a whole. None of the people whose opinion he valued went into raptures over it, but there were many who seemed genuine when they said they enjoyed it. As he sat watching it, he thought he could almost hear the heartbeat of the audience, and it was in tune with the rhythm on the stage. There were great moments, too, when he experienced the rapture of being able to communicate almost perfectly, and to have the evidence of such communication presented directly to his senses.

Whatever criticisms or notes of dissatisfaction he may have heard, there was one thing about which everybody agreed, and this was that the queen carried the entire show; yes, the queen, because she was not Gunavati any more, it was a transformation so miraculous, a transfiguration almost, in which her soul seemed to leave the confines of her frail body, and transcending the limits of space and time and of the karma that crushed her under its foot, to emerge in the fullest radiance, the highest dignity of the human spirit. To Virasena it was like the vision of Sambhoga Kaya, the Effulgent Body of the Buddha, vouchsafed only to the sincere devotee; a reward, as it were, for the unswerving faith with which he clung to her through many difficulties. As she walked from the darkness into the gleaming circle of light, to the rhythm of the drums, her hair tied in a top-knot and enclosed in a bejewelled tiara, her eyes, hovering over the audience like a pair of bees (as the poets of ancient times said), a murmur at first ran through the hall which then settled into perfect silence. Her voice had none of the harshness that he had noticed in it during rehearsals. The notes floated in the auditorium like the peal of a silver bell, and when she finished singing, the audience members, who normally never expressed their feelings, burst into spontaneous applause. There was no doubt that she had struck the right chord in their hearts. They waited for her appearance and greeted her every time she entered. And it was like that through to the end, when they rushed backstage to take a look at her, in a show of warmth and enthusiasm that was most unusual for Sinhalese playgoers.

Virasena, who normally left the scene of a production after the first night of its performance, leaving things in the hands of stage-managers and organizers. found himself slipping into the auditorium night after night as the lights dimmed; and when the drums beat their rhythm and the queen emerged from the darkness into the gleaming circle of light, it became to him an experience he had never known before, something unique in his entire life in the theatre. It was never the same on two consecutive nights, so that he felt impelled to go again and again. She seemed to be creating her role afresh on every occasion, so that he was never tired of watching her. And he realized that, in some indescribable way, the experience was of value to him, he stepped out of the theatre every night a different man, his emotions subdued and calm, his anxieties allayed, enjoying perfect peace, like an ascetic emerging from a *dhyana**.

After a while he began to feel that he constituted an integral element in any night's performance. She could give of her best because of his presence in the audience. She must first establish a rapport with him before she could establish a rapport with the rest. And he thought that as soon as she entered the stage her eyes ran through the audience looking for him, as if to get the cue from him like at rehearsals, and that it was only after they sought him out in his lonely seat and rested on him a moment that she was able to enter her role and perform her part. And he could almost see the faint light that flashed across her face when this secret rapport was established.

There were moments when he felt proud of her, proud as of something he had begotten and wrought into the shape of his heart's desire. When she sang he turned round at the audience and felt happy at heart to see clear evidence of admiration written on the people's faces. From the audience he expected a kind of gratitude, or at least a recognition that he had brought them a gem of purest ray serene from the depths of nowhere. But from her he expected nothing but the delight he experienced watching her. And he was satisfied with the secret acknowledgement she made that he was the source to which she owed her very being.

The image of the transformed Gunavati soon replaced, in his mind, that of the Gunavati he knew in real life, and he was unable to identify the one with the other. Whenever he saw the real Gunavati, she was the same plain wisp of a girl with her

---

* trance

aggressive voice and forward manner. Sometimes he kept on staring at her for a while, to see if the image of the queen would emerge from her, but it never did. There emerged only the same plain wisp of a girl about whom he had told his wife, she would never do for the queen's role. And he still felt he was right. He stopped thinking of the miracle that had occurred, and regarded the two as having separate identities.

V

The play ran about three months, with shows every week and sometimes on a day midweek. One day Samanmali said, with an unusual smile on her face, 'I think this play of yours will have some interesting by-products as well.'

'You mean romances. . .   marriages, and that sort of thing?' asked Virasena. 'Well, why not? After all, it has happened in all my plays.'

It was easy to see when attachments developed among members of the cast. They would be noticed chatting to each other in corners or would be seen coming to rehearsals and going back in each other's company. But Virasena had not noticed anything this time. From Samanmali's remarks he realized that things had been happening in the usual way, only they had taken care to see that nothing took place before his eyes. Perhaps because he played the role of moral adviser this time, he thought. Anyhow he shouldn't complain if they had observed some sort of propriety out of deference to him.

'There's someone interested in Gunavati, too,' said Samanmali after a while.

For a brief moment Virasena did not know what to say. 'O, is that so?' he blurted out at last, trying to hide the fact that he was surprised as well as disturbed by the news.

Samanmali did not venture any further information.

'Is it a member of the cast?' he asked, trying to sound as if he was not extraordinarily curious.

'Yes, it is Dharmapriya. Quite a handsome fellow. They'll make a fine couple.'

'Indeed, but these are the very people who despised her and thought it was below their dignity to keep company with her.'

'We may have been making too much of those incidents, in

our anxiety to stand up for Gunavati. I am sure it was because they didn't know her and she was an outsider more than because of social class and that sort of thing. You ought to see how good they are to her now, and what a polite lot of fellows they really are.'

'You know the saying that one kisses the hand one was not able to cut, don't you?' asked Virasena, rather sardonically.

But he chided himself almost immediately, saying that he had no reason to be bitter about the cast any more. They had turned out to be very cooperative and devoted, and he had long forgiven their lapses. If one of them was in love with Gunavati, he had no reason to resent it. But first of all he must find out at firsthand what was really happening. Samanmali's description may not be accurate, after all. Gunavati talked and moved about freely with everybody, and this may have given rise to the rumour.

For several days he watched Gunavati and Dharmapriya, but didn't notice that there was anything more than normal friendly relations between the two of them. He went backstage before the show, and was happy to observe that they had all cast away the inhibitions of their social life, and moved about like friends, calling each other by their first names, joking with one another and sharing the make-up because some had finished their own and others had forgotten to bring theirs. But this was only as long as he could observe them unseen. Samanmali always went in to the dressing-room and helped the girls with their costumes and make-up. He peeped in and found her busy. She was happy joking with the girls, but their laughter ceased when they saw his face at the door.

Suddenly he felt sad and lonely. It is true he used to tell them that his work was over on the first night, and that they must carry on thenceforth without him. But the chance of it actually happening seemed still remote, and he had never tried to envisage what it would be like if it really happened. Now he began to wonder whether he had not actually come face-to-face with such a situation. He began to dimly realize that the play could go on without him. It was like the flow of life itself that left behind the unwanted, left behind even those who had done their task and were no more wanted, and flowed on.

Then one evening something happened that brought about a strange revulsion within Virasena. It was an evening scheduled for a performance of his play. There was hardly forty-five minutes to go before the play was due to start, but Gunavati hadn't arrived. Her entry took place about fifteen minutes after the opening and there was much to do regarding her make-up and costume. Samanmali was looking anxious, and Virasena asked her, 'Where is she?' almost as if he were reproaching her for Gunavati's delay.

'I don't know,' she replied. Her thoughts appeared to be far away.

'Didn't she come home?'

Gunavati dropped into see Samanmali at least twice or thrice a week, usually when Virasena was away.

'Not for the last several days.'

'I hope she is not ill.' A sudden fear seized Virasena.

'No, she is not ill. Somebody would have told me if she was. She'll come for the play. Don't worry. . . I don't know why she is late, though.'

Virasena wondered if his wife was hiding something from him.

In a short while they saw her coming and she was in the company of Dharmapriya. Virasena didn't ask any questions. He merely said, 'You have just about half an hour, Gunavati. So hurry.'

She was dressed in a saree of a soft silver-grey material which draped gently about her, showing the curves of her hips and bosom. The usual pig-tail was not there, and, instead, her hair was tied in a heavy knot which rested on the nape of her neck. He realised, in a flash, that she was not any more the wisp of a girl he had always taken her to be, that she was grown into a woman who spread charm and sex around her as she walked. And a painful feeling gnawed at his heart as if something that was part of his flesh was being torn away by force.

He went backstage a few minutes before the performance, to see if Gunavati had been able to get ready in time, and from a conversation he overheard inadvertently, he learned why she had been late. She had been to the cinema with Dharmapriya.

His head swam as the facts became plain to him. But he quickly took stock of himself. And when the lights were dimmed he slipped as usual into his accustomed seat in the auditorium. But it was not the same any more. It was not the queen who walked this time from the darkness into the gleaming circle of light and sought him out with her bee-like eyes. The two images which had remained separated in his mind, so far, now merged into one, and he saw neither the queen nor the wisp of a girl, but the woman Gunavati whom he had seen in the company of another.

For a few days he struggled with himself. If Gunavati found a good husband, he told himself, it ought to be the most desirable culmination of his patronage of her. And Dharmapriya was a handsome, well-mannered young man with a job which would enable him to make her comfortable. Why should he feel disturbed about their courtship?

But he was weak. He felt lonely and left out, and he wanted his dream back at all costs. He had an idea. It was mean and wicked. But he was impelled to put it into practice. He called Samanmali and spoke to her solemnly. He didn't believe any of the things he said, but he had to act the part.

'I have been worried the last few days about this matter of Gunavati,' he began. 'You know, I wouldn't have minded it if it was anybody else. I have never before bothered about the personal affairs of my cast, and have never taken responsibility for them. . . . This affair between Gunavati and Dharmapriya. . . . you seem to have known about it. . . how serious do you think Dharmapriya is? Have you any idea what his intentions are?'

'Well, Gunavati told me he has actually proposed marriage to her. That's why I didn't mind even their going to the cinema together.'

'O, I see. So you knew all about it? I only guessed you knew more than I did.'

'Yes, I knew about it, and was glad for the girl. Don't you think it's a good thing for her?'

'I have my doubts about it. And that is why I wanted to talk to you. How can we take the responsibility for such a thing? How much do we know about Dharmapriya? I have a feeling he only wants to have a good time. He will drop her after that. He seems to be a gay sort of young chap.'

'Then why should he have proposed to her?'

'What do you mean by saying he has proposed? And what is the worth of such proposals? Naturally the girl's head will turn when someone like Dharmapriya shows an interest in her. Who said he proposed? Did you ask him?'

'No, I didn't ask him. That's what Gunavati told me.'

'There you are. It's what she has imagined in her excitement. Do you believe, for a moment, that a man like Dharmapriya will ever want to marry a girl like Gunavati? Don't you know how class-conscious these people are? Has he ever visited her parents and talked to them?'

'No, I didn't think so. It's too early, isn't it?'

'Why should it be too early? They shouldn't go to the pictures together unless they have got their parents' sanction. I think it is better if you wash your hands off the matter. I wouldn't take the responsibility. Obviously they have been getting about together like this because they thought they had your approval. And perhaps mine, through you.'

Samanmali remained silent and Virasena felt he was gaining his point. He continued. 'Let's not rush these things too much,' he said, thinking it would be politic to concede somewhat to her. 'Let us see whether Dharmapriya is sincere. Let them wait a little longer. After all, Gunavati is still young. She must get to know these people better. This is probably the first time she has ever moved about with young men. Have you made any inquiries about Dharmapriya?'

Samanmali suddenly realized that she knew nothing of Dharmapriya, and began to get cold feet. 'No, I haven't been going around making systematic inquiries. After all, I am not a professional match-maker,' she said in defence of herself.

'Well, I have heard certain things said about him,' said Virasena, and he was inventing. 'These things reach my ears somehow. He has had previous love affairs, and one with a married woman.'

As Samanmali didn't say anything, he continued, 'That is why I say we have to be careful before we go on encouraging this kind of thing. Maybe he is just trying to exploit the situation because Gunavati, being a simple village girl, will be flattered by his attentions and will not have the courage to refuse him.'

It was Virasena's wish that his wife should talk to Gunavati and advise her about the pitfalls that young girls from the village must watch for, and about gallant men who make offers of marriage. She and Gunavati were closeted together for nearly an hour, and when they came out, Samanmali told her husband that Gunavati had given the assurance that she would drop her affair with Dharmapriya.'

At the earliest opportunity Virasena summoned the young

man and talked to him.

'It is not my habit to interfere in your personal matters,' he began, 'but when something is happening I feel it is my responsibility to give young people the kind of advice they need. I have to tell you something about Gunavati. I haven't breathed a word of it to any body, but it is my duty not to withhold this information any longer from you, because I can see that you are getting emotionally involved with her. She was very ill sometime back, more ill than anybody knew. Actually the doctor found that she had tuberculosis. You know how it is. Of course, he says she is all right now, but one can never tell. It is hard to eradicate this kind of disease completely when it gets hold of you once. Besides, the tendency to contract it can even be transmitted to one's children. . . . This is entirely between you and me. I don't want to spread any talk that could spoil the girl's chances of marriage in the future.'

As he talked, he watched Dharmapriya's face, and saw growing on it, gradually, an expression of abject fear as he began to realize the import of Virasena's words. And Virasena was glad that his manoeuvre was succeeding.

VI

Thus Virasena had his dream restored back to him. Gunavati was never seen any more in the company of Dharmapriya, and Virasena noticed that they didn't so much as greet each other when they met. He wondered why that was so; he hadn't asked them not to be friends, after all. Was it that Dharmapriya felt that Gunavati had deceived him by with-holding from him the information about her illness? And in the evenings, when the performance began, he slipped into his accustomed seat in the darkness, and watched once again his queen come striding majestically into the gleaming circle of light, to the deep rolling of the drums. And his heart leaped when he saw how her eyes scanned the audience and finally rested on him, and how she then resumed her walk with added confidence; the rapport was established once more. He had found his queen again, the queen he had brought out of the darkness into the gleaming circle of light and enthroned there.

The play ran for about a year, reaching the height of its

popularity after about the sixth month. Virasena went with it to remote corners of the island, and sat in dusty auditoriums, staring at dirty and torn curtains in the midst of noisy and unruly audiences, waiting for his queen to appear. And when she did, the sordidness around him vanished, and his mind was suffused with the vision before him.

One day they were discussing how they ought to celebrate the fiftieth performance of the play which was to be a fortnight ahead, when Subasinghe casually remarked, 'Let's do it in grand style. After all, it is a double occasion.'

Virasena was somewhat puzzled. 'What's the other occasion?' he asked, blinking affectedly.

Subasinghe and the rest didn't reply. They looked from one to the other and smiled. Virasena began to feel uncomfortable. 'What's so funny, anyway?' he asked. He sounded vexed.

At last Subasinghe spoke. 'We thought you knew all the while and were pretending. . . . Gunavati got married to Dharmapriya,' he said.

'Really? When?'

'Nearly four or five months ago. They are going to set up house shortly, we are told.'

'Oh, that's fine. . . . I didn't know anything. . . . Nobody tells me anything nowadays. . . . Of course, we must celebrate.'

Virasena's immediate impulse was to ask Samanmali whether the information he had received was correct, and if so, whether she had herself known of it all the time. But he hesitated as he thought more and more of it. Instead, he feigned excuses and stayed home without going to the performances any more. When Samanmali came back after the shows and gave him glowing accounts of how the play was received, and how Gunavati did better than ever before, he felt once more sad and lonely and left out.

Then one day Gunavati and Dharmapriya came to see him, and, offering him betel leaves, fell down at his feet and paid him obeisance. He touched their heads and blessed them smiling.

'You kept the secret very well, I must say,' he said, and added, 'you must take part in my next play as hero and heroine. Then people need not keep on guessing whether the hero is married to the heroine in real life or not.'

—*Translated by the author*

Karuna Perera

A Light in the Darkness

I've put the dal on to cook and am watching the road from the garden. From here you can see a long way down the road. No sign of Mother yet. On the veranda Granny is pounding away at her chew of betel leaves and areca nut. The iron pestle strikes the wooden mortar with a hollow sound. Granny's bottom touches the mud floor as she squats on her haunches.

'Come back in the house. . . I don't suppose Mother will be much longer. . . .'

'She's never been as late as this before.'

I'm sitting by Granny, staring at the garden. She is still bent over the mortar, still making that hollow sound with her pounding. Slowly the darkness comes flooding in to our very feet. A desolate moment this, when the dead sound of the iron on the wooden mortar rouses feelings of inexpressible sadness. . . .

'I've cooked some dal. I don't know what else to give you, Granny, since you can't eat chillies and hot things like that.'

'Just wait awhile, your mother's sure to bring something.'

'She didn't have any money. I had to give her five cents for the bus.'

'Ah, well, I dare say she'll borrow something from somebody.'

'Yes, I dare say she will.' Resigned, I continue gazing at the road. If Mother got into debt this week as well. . . . she'd use her wages to settle her debts and then be at a loss. I feel like fingering my dress. Whenever I have to bend down it splits apart with a ripping noise. Sweat and hair oil have rotted the cloth through and through. Yesterday Mother asked me to wear my best visiting dress about the house. But I know she won't be able to make me another dress just yet.

When it's the turn of the family next door to give alms to the temple, they take me along to do the washing up. From the time

I get there I do nothing but wash dishes till my back's nearly broken, but I still like going to the temple. That's because I never get a chance to go anywhere else. If I wore my visiting dress in the house, what would I wear to the temple? How would Mother be able to make me a new dress as quickly as she'd say she could?

While I am thinking about such things, I suddenly remember the dal I've just left cooking. I leave the veranda and go to the fire to stir the pot.

'Are you off to the temple then, Hamine?'

'Yes. . . just take hold of this temple offering, will you. . . . Where's the girl?'

Granny is talking to the old woman next door. I come running forward.

'Pick me those two flowers as well, my dear.'

It isn't with very good grace that I pick the flowers and put them in her basket. They were the first flowers on my rose bush, two little red blossoms. Without a trace of feeling she had drained my hendirikka bush of all its flowers too. I must tell Granny what the pious old hag had done in the morning.

'What a waste of my flowers, giving them to that stingy old crone. This morning when Mother asked if she could lend her fifty cents to go to work, she croaked out "Na-aw" almost before Mother had finished asking the question. But she's got plenty of money to buy offerings for the monks. It's all your fault, Granny, letting her have my flowers.'

'Be silent, child, and don't fill yourself up with sin.'

'Why, don't we lend money sometimes? As soon as Mother gets her wages where does she go straightaway but to give alms? But *they* give their alms like a kind of loan, expecting to get it back with interest in the next life. We'll get to nirvana before these fine madams, Granny.'

'Just listen to her—well, you've certainly grown too much too soon, my girl. Let's just keep ourselves to ourselves and not meddle in other people's affairs.'

I sit on the veranda once more, looking out on to the road. Granny has stopped pounding. The betel leaves are now in her gaping mouth. Thinking about the neighbours and their doings, I recall what a fine fellow our bread-man is. He comes from a long way off to sell bread from house to house, but he never hesitates to give us credit. He knows that Mother will settle up with him as soon as she is paid. I've had enough now of eating bread soaked in strong dark tea. But no other person would give us credit except that man.

The old woman next door once did my mother a fine turn. I must say, it makes me boil, just to think about it. But I'm just not firm enough to say 'no' when she asks me to go with her to the temple.

Returning home with her wages, Mother had gone round by next door's kitchen in order to pay off a debt. Needless to say, she did that every time she got paid. That evening the old woman did something she'd never done before. She offered Mother a seat and a glass of tea—with milk. Somehow she managed to coax my mother into grinding her chillies for her that evening. Since that time I've always hated the old hag. Mother's poor hands, so sore from handling sand and cement, began to smart from the chillies and her eyes filled with tears. That's what she's like, that old woman. Whenever her serving-woman is away, the cunning old crone always manages to get someone else to do all the things that need doing.

I cried as I put coconut oil on Mother's palms. She's exhausted by the time she gets home each day, I know, so I don't let her do any work around the house. I have something hot ready for her to eat as soon as she comes home.

I remember the dal again. I must take it off the fire and cover it. Wonder why Mother's not home yet. . . . Granny's still on the veranda munching her betel. The dark has spread throughout the house, it's time to light a lamp.

'Granny, I wonder why Mother's not yet. . . .'

'You just go and see to the lamp.'

I get up to light the bottle-lamp, put it on the table and go back to Granny. All sorts of weird imaginings come into my head. The light from the bottle-lamp does not fall here on the veranda. So the fantastical thoughts in my head writhe and wrestle unchallenged.

. . . Someone killed when a scaffold fell. . . another buried under a mound of earth and taken to the hospital. . . an old man with his leg maimed by a mammoty stroke. . . a woman with an arm broken when she slipped while carrying a panful of sand on her head. . . . All these thoughts came together, ravelling my mind.

I want to get up and look out towards the road again. But I

haven't the strength in my legs to get up. I look up at Granny's face, wanting to say something. But I am unable to speak a word. My lips and mouth are dry. In this darkness I can hardly see even Granny's face. I couldn't say for certain how long I remained tired and apathetic like this, staring out into the dark and desolate garden.

A vague and ghostly shape moves in the darkness. Suddenly it appears in view through the weak light of the bottle-lamp. It is Mother.

I get up quickly and take the bag that was in Mother's hand. Granny is still on the veranda. Mother sits down there, too, and from out of the darkness calls for a glass of water. I haven't the heart to ask her why she is late. Carrying the bag, I turn to go indoors. A lovely light shines from the bottle-lamp on the table. It sparkles all over the house. I think it shines all the brighter in here because of the darkness enfolding the veranda. As I return with a jug of water for Mother, my eyes are dazzled by the light, probably because I have been sitting out in the dark for so long.

'I got ten rupees. Carolis said the boss wants me to come again next week.'

'That's all very well, but you must ask for more wages.'

'It can't be done at once. I'll speak to Carolis about it after awhile.'

'Much better to speak up for yourself instead of letting Carolis do it.'

'No, the boss is a fine man, he won't ignore me, I'm sure of that.'

Water jug in hand I eavesdrop on these private whisperings between Granny and Mother. But I don't really understand all of it. 'What's it all about?' I ask, going up to Mother. Without a word she take the water jug from my hand. Her coarse fingers brush against mine. They are very cold. A fragrance, like that from a fine face powder, hangs about her. I'm wafted along by it and my thoughts float into space. . . .

'Do you have to work very late at night now, Mother. . . ? They must be in a hurry to hand the building over then.'

'Never mind that, you get on with cutting up that fish.'

Silently, I go indoors. Borne along by the smell of the fish in the bag, my thoughts once more lose their way and become stranded on their journey. So I didn't need to go on that journey. Why set out when you've no clear idea of the road or resting place? But my mother, who didn't have five cents for her fare in the morning, comes home at nightfall with a fine para fish in the bag. . . . The fish is tasty enough, but it stinks all the same.

I can't forget what Granny and Mother were whispering about. I take the fish out of the bag, chop it up, wash and prepare it and put it on the fire. Small bits of bread soaked in the fish gravy would be just the thing. . . . I put pieces of broken coconut shells on the fire. The flames leap up with a roar. The whole house is filled with light. There's more light than from the bottle-lamp. But Mother and Granny have still not come in from that darkness.

—*Translated by Gamini Salgado*

Simon Navagattegama

The Addict

Evening was coming. 'Cortal*' David had a lot of work. Peasants, their bodies damp with their day's labour, crowded on to his porch in an endless flow. Bottles of *kasippu*** lay hidden among the bushes of his overgrown yard. From time to time he brought one out from among the bushes. The liquor, poured down in a special manner from dirt-stained glasses, seeped into the bodies of his clients, searing their throats and stomachs. The one or two rupees knotted in the corners of their *amudas*+ fell into 'Cortal' David's lap. Some, wiping their mouths and slowly stroking their empty bellies, fingered the edge of their now unknotted kerchiefs as they stepped outside for the liquor to take its effect, savouring it on their tongues. The confusion of a market-place reigned.

Sadana, sipping his half-bottle since the early afternoon, lay sprawled in a corner of 'Cortal' David's yard. Unlike the others, he did not drink from a glass. As usual David had filled his regular half-bottle for him. He took it in his hand, hugged it close, and sipped it slowly. Slowly, the tiredness subsided. He began to feel the *kasippu* permeate his whole body. He liked to lie there contemplating, while the veins in his body slowly became intoxicated. After the 'current' reached a certain point, he got up from his sprawling position. Life came slowly back to his lips. There was so much to talk about with those coming and going in here. His shaky legs moved back and forth all over 'Cortal' David's yard till night was far advanced. He got himself

---

*the brand name of a kind of aspirin or pep pill—used also in illicit brews and used here as a nickname; ** an illicit brew; + a large-sized handkerchief used by farmers as a loincloth when working in muddy rice-fields, but which also functions as a handkerchief or scarf at other times

entangled in the feet of some, banged into others, was flung this way and that.

'Cortal' David treated Sadana better then he did anyone else. His half-bottle was always of the best matured stuff. It would be further thickened with a few grams of *kansa**. Sadana had grown used to the mild headache caused by the *kansa*. For over five years now he had been addicted to this drink.

Till he was forty years old Sadana had lived life alone—free as a bird in the sky. At forty he acquired a good wife. For eight years he lived a happily married life. Apart from the moderate drinking habit acquired in his bachelor days, and the regret that they were childless, there had been little to mar their happiness. Then, one day, his wife fell a victim to a serious disease. He spent all he had on her. He mortgaged the only piece of land he owned to 'Cortal' David in order to treat her illness. If she had recovered, by now everything would have turned out well. But instead she became an incurable invalid. Then a great change came over him too.

The one-eighth glass of arrack, which had been his daily drink, now increased to a half-bottle. For two or three days in the week, he worked a half-day or as a hired labourer. It was all that was needed for him to sustain his now unwanted existence.

His wife, liked a wasted rag, groaned and moaned, wheezing inside the house. She came alive only at sundown. From then on there was no escape for him. Enraged like a demoness, she would turn on him, shouting abuse all night long, as if taking revenge for some old grudge. She would grind her teeth and cling to him, and her shouts and abuse would ring out into the night. At the same time, however, she would cook whatever he brought home, serve it and push the plate towards him. It was only when he was eating that Sadana showed signs of life. For the rest, as if to avoid his wife's constant pestering, he lazily preserved his drunker stupor. He was accustomed now to living, merely by raising or lowering the level of his intoxication to match his wife's anger.

During this long period of change, 'Cortal' David treated him as a good friend. Sadana's house and garden now belonged to

---

* ganja (*cannabis*)

'Cortal' David. It was three years and five months since the mortgage had expired but he said nothing about it to Sadana. He made no claim on the land. From the day he became owner of the property, however, he stopped charging Sadana for his half-bottle of *kasippu*. That was the only difference. Nor did Sadana ever stop to inquire either from "Cortal" David or himself, 'Have my house and land became 'Cortal' David's property? Have I not been drinking *kasippu* at no charge these past three-and-a-half years?' Instead, he lived as one who had consciously chosen to forget everything regarding his life. There was nothing he would not talk about when drunk, yet he said not a word about himself, not even when drunk, because as a matter of fact he had nothing of importance to say about himself.

'Ha. . . Rana. . . ,' he would exclaim, tottering slowly towards a companion who was sinking a cup of *kasippu* in the yard. 'Why such a long face these days? And your head hanging down so dejectedly. Is something the matter?'

'Yes, old man,' Rana would reply, tilting his head back to pour the last few drops into his mouth. 'Two of my girls are very sick, man. Besides, the wife is now in her ninth month. I don't know what to do. When I go home I don't get a moment's sleep. The wife with her hand to her back goes out and gathers herbs and all night long I have to crush them and brew concoctions for them.'

'Why, man, with so much to do how can you wander around here drinking *kasippu*? Who is the doctor treating them? What is the matter with them?' And Rana would engage in a detailed account of the illness.

'Yes, yes, that's a terrible thing. If you don't treat it immediately those two lovely girls will be lost.' Sadana would listen to Rana's woes and advise him. 'Go to Galigomuwa. Get them some medicine from the Gampaha doctor and see what happens. He is a good doctor. If he once puts his hand to it there's nothing more you need to worry about.' Sadana would then spit on all sides of the yard and the spittle would hit the feet of anyone who happened to be passing by.

'You had better take some serious interest in caring for those little ones. It's no joke. Drinking Cortal and walking around won't help you. You are a family man. Maintaining a family is not as easy as drinking Cortal.' Rambling on in this manner he would finally take his empty bottle and hand it back to David.

David had no time to stand talking to him. He had to keep his ears alert to distinguish whether the sound in the distance was the bus from Abogama or the police jeep. Besides, he had to pour out the drinks for those still climbing up on his porch; give them their individual portions of diluted or strengthened *kassippu* and collect the money for it. He had to keep a mental note of the accounts of all those people. Every single empty bottle had to be hidden back in the bushes. Hidden so that even the blows of the policeman's iron pick would not uncover them. Fresh bottles had to be brought out from their hiding-places. In spite of all this work, however, he would not fail to exchange a word or two with Sadana.

'How's your drink?'

'Just right. Excellent,' Sadana would reply. He would then show his teeth in a grin.

'Hee. . . hee. . . hee. . . hee. . . ,' David would reply with a similar laugh. 'Is there too much *kansa*?' he would ask.

'No. . . . no. . . . it's the usual amount, eh? Hee . . . hee. . . hee. . . .'

'Eh. . . hee. . . hee. . . ha. . . ha. . . .'

David never spoke to him about anything other than the *kasippu*. Sadana too talked of nothing else. This limited exchange would indicate to both the strong bonds of friendship and understanding that existed between them. The fact that both of them could laugh the same laugh was proof of it.

Night fell. It was time for Sadana to go home. A shudder ran through him. As if to brush it aside he stretched himself, ran his fingers through his matted hair and pushed it forward on to his forehead and over his eyes. He then set out on his way.

The path was indistinct in the darkness. But though he did not see it, he did not lose his way. How strange it would be if he did lose his way and arrived at some other place. Whatever that would mean to his stomach, what a pleasure it would be to his eyes and ears! His wife, who crouched all day like a bundle of dirty rags on the tattered mat, came alive in the evening and would now be on the lookout for him as usual. Moisture was bad for her wheeze so she never bathed, never washed her face. She was not a human being. With her hair dishevelled and her eyes like flaming coals, red with pain and rage, she rose up like a ghost before his mind's eye. He shuddered again. If only he could miss the road and arrive somewhere else. However, even in the most bitter blackness, just as the hand inevitably takes the lump of rice straight to the mouth with its thirty-two teeth, so his legs would take him to his own broken-down hut.

His house and yard were a hell-hole. A demoness resided there. His wife was no longer the good and kind woman he had formerly known. She had been bedridden for a long time. At some point during her illness the good woman he knew must have died. This was not she. It was a ghost arisen on her death. There are different kinds of spirits, many of them weak. This one was complete with all the powers of the most terrible demons. Although in the past five years he had returned each evening to his house, that graveyard presided over by her, yet he had still not learned to co-exist with her in it. He would never get used to it.

Each evening as he turned into his yard, for the past five years, a shudder passed through him. Each morning he would leave the house with a great sense of relief. Even on days he was not working he never came back home before nightfall.

His wife, moaning, would lie all day in a corner, writhing in pain. She never called on the gods or cried out her woes. There was no relief for her. She would hoard all her aches and pains and the pressures that wracked her mind. But with the cool of the evening, as if by divine dispensation, these aches and pains vanished. Then, apart from the wheezing, her other ailments disappeared.

At the very hour when Sadana's veins were revitalized by the half-bottle of *kasippu*, her limbs, too, seemed to come alive. She would get up laboriously and light the fire. Then she would crane her neck and look out for her husband's return. He did not come before dark. With the burning fire in the hearth her anger would also flare, rise and totally engulf her. She would clear her throat, blow her nose and prepare her voice and tongue for the attack. It mattered little whether there was provocation for her anger or not. She was enraged without reason. Her mind was fixed in the quite unfair conviction that this hell she had fallen into was all of Sadana's creation. She knew that each evening her husband liked his water hot. So she filled a pot and put it on the fire. Then she cooked whatever he had brought her the previous day. But even as the water in the pot began to heat, dance and hiss, the anger within her would seethe and overflow, bringing words of harsh abuse to her lips. The abuse and scoldings that began at this point would continue unceasingly until late into the night. Sadana heard it even after he fell asleep. If she sensed that he was no longer hearing her abuse she would throw a broom or some other object at him.

'Uuh. . . woman. . . I wonder why my back is not broken. . . ?' was all he would say. The dry cough that arose intermittently with the wheezing, combined with her loud-voiced anger, would rise in shrill rank abuse that shattered his ears, resound in the far corners of the village and then slowly subside.

All this, as if according to a divinely ordained time-table, had been a daily occurrence throughout these past five years. He had not yet, however, grown accustomed to any of it.

As if to delay his arrival at home he walked very slowly.

As he would draw nearer to the house, the demon form of his wife standing at the door and glaring like a rabid bitch at his approach would become distinct, and appear ever more frightening. He would then struggle to increase the stupor that enveloped him in order to fortify his faltering mind. The half-bottle of 'special' and whatever amount of *kansa* there had been in it would seem nothing to him. One could not look a demoness in the face unless one's level of intoxication was more than whatever one had consumed. Even the great warrior Gotaimbara went to face Mahasona, the graveyard demon, only after consuming sixteen casks of liquor. Like all seasoned drinkers, Sadana could raise and lower the level of his intoxication at will. On catching sight of her he would raise his drunkenness to the point where he could hardly stand straight.

'So you have come back—have you—drunk, and after darkness has fallen? You have come, have you?' his wife would greet him in a voice that would make his teeth chatter as it mingled with the grating sound of her asthmatic wheeze. 'And are you now drunk as a fish?'

His mind would struggle to run and hide in some deserted corner where it would not have to listen to her terrifying and deadly lamentations. But with great effort he would forcibly bring himself to enter the doorway of the house.

The yard was full of tall overgrown bushes. One or two broken edaru sticks lying around was all that was left of what had once been a fence. He shut his ears and eyes, wrapped himself in his drunkenness and prepared to enter the house.

The next minute he looked in astonishment at the house. There was not a hint of a light inside. It was pitch black; not a glimmer. For a moment he stood still, then walked slowly through the yard. He stood outside and tried to peer into the nooks and crannies of the dilapidated house shrouded in darkness. He could see nothing. As the earth bathed all day by the heat of a fierce sun finally emits a faint sigh of relief as it mingles with the cool of the darkness, so a feeble moan emanating from a corner of the house fell on his ears. A vague lonely fear arose in him.

'Hey. . . !' The sound of his own voice amazed him. For more than five years now, certainly not less, he had never spoken to his wife on entering the house. His drunkenness instantly vanished, he knew not where. His foot knocked against the edge of the porch as he climbed up on it. The moan came from within the house. He ran here and there confusedly. What should he do? Nothing was happening today as it had happened on all other previous evenings. The usual routine was snapped. He looked far and near as if trying to decide what to do.

'Hey! Do you hear me?' The words slipped from him again. It was the manner in which he used to call out to her five years ago. But her moaning merely increased.

He moved towards the kitchen and felt around where he thought the fireplace was. A piece of firewood buried under the ashes struck his hand. He picked it up, blew on it once or twice and saw it spark. After trying for a long time he managed to get the fire going. Then he found the bottle-lamp, lit it, and with lamp in hand walked quickly into the bedroom. He barely managed to stop himself from tripping over the threshold and falling over. As if blind and unable to see, he held the lamp up, gazing at her from head to foot.

'What is wrong with you?' he asked in a trembling voice. 'What is it?'

She was breathing fast. Her withered upper body was naked. She clung to her breasts with her ten sticks of fingers. With each inhalation her ribs and chest bones, with the veins etched against them showing through her dissolving flesh, swelled up like a skeleton.

'I'm very sick,' she muttered with parched lips. A dry breath, as from a bellows, emanated 'shu. . . us. . .' from her nostrils and mouth. There was not an ounce of flesh on her face. The mop of her hair, tangled and dishevelled like a mad woman's, covered her forehead. His hand instinctively went towards it. Squatting, holding the lamp in one hand, he stroked her hair back with the other. 'Shall I give you some water?' His trembling voice was full of grief. The *kasippu* he had drunk a moment ago now came churning up in his throat. He was aware of it, but not as before. There was no intoxication in it. Nor did it have the strength of anything more than a gulp of water rising up to his throat.

He took the lamp, went to the kitchen and brought a little water. He then fed her some drops on her lips. He took a pillow filled with rice husks lying nearby, lifted her head and placed it on the pillow. He then sat beside her, his face peering into hers. For a long time they were both silent. Having received these attentions from him her face slowly underwent a change. Twisted with pain as it was, a certain peace came over it. Her lips which were a concentration of her grief now took on a faint shadow of joy. Sadana saw how certain pleasing lines that in the past five years had vanished from her face, appeared there again behind its harsh furrows. She was wasted with sickness and age. But as he looked at her he saw a certain glimmer of the loving wife he had known five years ago.

She seemed somewhat relieved after drinking the water. The rising and falling of her breath slowed down. Her hand rose to touch his hand which was resting on his knee. The tears that came to her eyes were like joyous dewdrops touched by the sun as they danced in the light of the lamp. 'You must be very tired after digging all day,' she faltered.

'No, I. . . ' he tried to say something. There was nothing to say. Even if there had been anything to say his throat was choked with grief.

'Put some water on the fire, there is a little tea left in that tin. Pour yourself some tea. In a little while when I can hold my head up, I will make a roti for you.'

'No. . . it is not necessary.'

Again, for a long while, there was nothing said between them. She continued to look only into his eyes. There was not a sound or movement around them. Apart from the breath escaping through her lips, even the air outside seemed still. The lamp gave forth a dim light and the wick burned perfectly straight.

'The past several years have been a bad period for us.'

'Yes,' he said watching the hollows and cliffs of her face as they changed with the shadows. He had now quite forgotten that he had even drunk *kasippu* that evening.

'The stars gave us a bad period.'

'Yes. . . .'

'It was our karma at the root of all this. They say even if one is a Buddha one pays for one's past actions.'

'Yes, it is our karma that was the cause of it all. The consequences of our deeds follow us like our shadows.'

Neither of them used the word 'I' or 'my', but 'we' and 'our'. The rift that had existed between them for five years now closed in a moment. An understanding deeper than had ever existed between them was slowly growing, giving rise to hopes of a new future. But for her illness, they would at this moment have been the happiest couple alive.

She still held his hand and stayed a long while without speaking. Perhaps because of the absence of the former unmitigated barrage of sound that hurt his ears he seemed to sense a certain emptiness, as of ghosts standing around him. The understanding that had arisen between them was so strong, however, that he sensed the emptiness only vaguely. This understanding seemed to both of them to grow stronger as much in their moments of long silence as when they exchanged a word or two.

Aroused by a vague feeling of grief that seemed to combine with the silence, he tried to clothe the skeleton lying before him with the flesh, blood and former vitality of the woman he had known.

With difficulty she turned her head, and sustaining herself with her groans she looked around her. The soot-blackened walls, the dilapidated roof draped in cobwebs and hanging strands of eye-flies met her gaze. A lump of straw hung down between two beams. One part of the wall, washed out by the rain dripping from the roof, was devoid of all its wattle and mud covering.

'Alas, our house is all dilapidated. . . hm. . . hm. . . hm . . . hm. . . . do you remember we talked about it before my illness? How we would enlarge the old house and renovate it. Remember we decided to raise the front roof, put another row of rafters and some posts and widen the veranda? Then there'd be plenty of room in front. Visitors could sit comfortably and even eat there. When we would need a feast for a work-gang, ten or fifteen would be able to stretch out comfortably and eat at one sitting.'

'Yes,' Sadana confirmed. Surprisingly, he had forgotten that both his house and the land had long since been mortgaged and now belonged to 'Cortal' David. His wife, however, did not know that her husband had mortgaged it, so she could talk about renovating it, enlarging it and adding to it without any reservations. How was it that Sadana could readily agree with her suggestions, without qualification? 'We can do it even now. It's not such a big job, is it? Once we cut a few well-seasoned andara saplings as timber for the rafters it is done. After that it is merely a matter of cutting a few dummalla sticks for the roof and then thatching it with straw. If we go to a threshing floor we can get a hundred bundles or more. Once we thatch the whole roof this leak here will stop. All we have to do first is cut some kuratiya sticks and andara saplings,' she replied.

He too, as if to better appreciate her suggestions, cast his eyes around the house. He discussed her ideas, disagreed with some of her suggestions.

'No no. . . kuratiya sticks are no good for rafters. We can chop some good wira saplings. Even for the posts tharana is better than dummalla. Tharana does not decay. It lasts a hundred years. We might as well do a job that will last while we are about it. I'm thinking we'll not just do the front roof, but we'll extend the roof all round the house and add porches. Then we'll have a veranda all round with the room in the centre. Wouldn't that be good? It will be like Heena's house. Then you can have plenty of space on the veranda to pound, winnow, work or stretch around.'

In this manner for the better part of the night the two of them, hand in hand, talked of renovating their house. At last, he began to feel sleepy. Without bothering to close the door he stretched himself out beside her.

Stopping from time to take a breath between wheezes, she continued to talk. While her husband worked on the timber she would go and get the red mud for redoing the walls and the floor of the porches. She described at great length how she would do this to perfection, without a flaw.

She stopped talking only when she heard her husband snoring in his sleep. Releasing her fingers from his grasp with difficulty, she tugged at a rag lying close by, and covered her chest and neck with it. For a long time she did not fall asleep. Remembering the distant past, she wept tears of joy. Remembering the new future they had inaugurated that day she wept more tears of joy. She felt the pain in her chest increase but she never once thought to wake her husband. The flame, drawing up the last drop of oil in the bottom of the lamp, flared up from time to time while it was burning out. Two or three times she twisted around with difficulty and coughed. For a long while she panted. In the light of the dying flame she continued to gaze at the darkening face of her husband. 'The blessings of the Triple Gem. . . ,' she muttered. 'May the blessings of the Triple Gem. . . .'

Sleep completely overpowered Sadana's wearied limbs where he lay stretched out. Because of the dramatic change that had taken place that evening, after five years, he did not feel the intoxication of the *kasippu*. But when he lay lifeless in sleep the *kansa* together with the *kasippu* running through his veins began to exert their power. Crazed by the potion he had drunk, his mind worked all night long, cutting timber for the house. He extended the roof around the house, added the porches exactly as he and his wife had decided. His wife stood by him helping.

Waking in the morning, as if trying to clarify something, he lay as he was, thinking. He was sleeping on his back, looking up. In the distant village the cocks were crowing. Cows were mooing in answer. The door was still open as it had been all night. Banks of morning sunshine came in at the door. His wife slept in the midst of a bundle of rags, stiff as a log. The customary wheeze no longer emanated from her. Her hand which had fallen on his body was cold as ice. He tried to lift it and lay it aside, still in his sleepy state, but he could not move it. It was as stiff as if cut in wood. He sat up instantly and peered into her face. Her eyes were closed. Apart from the jaw bones and the bones of the forehead, in her immobile face the rest was sunken. In one corner of her nostrils were drops of liquid, like beads of sweat.

For a long time, as if unable to gain control of his mind, he gazed at her.

'What have you done to yourself?' he muttered like one not quite in his right mind. Then, taking up the rags lying in a corner, he covered the skeleton which was all that was left of her face. A sound like a sob escaped his lips. He did not cry. Like one who had made a firm resolution he stood up quickly. He tightened his waist-cloth, slung his sarong round his neck, took the handkerchief lying nearby, combed back the grey locks falling all over his forehead, and tied it around his head. The handkerchief, perhaps because of being constantly dampened by sweat and water, was crumpled.

He closed the door carefully and stepped out.

'I will do it all. I will renovate the house just as she said. . . .' he muttered to himself, not even bothering to glance at the roof he was planning to extend. He went out on the road.

Sadana went straight to 'Cortal' David's house. David had just awakened. He was cleaning out some bottles with sand. Sadana always came to see him in the evening. Today he had changed his customary habit, so David looked at him with interest. He could glean nothing from Sadana's withered face covered with sweat and care. There was a certain determination in his eyes, however, not seen before.

'I want your axe and knife.'

'Cortal' David looked in surprise at Sadana's face. Sadana's manner of speech was also changed.

'I am going to the jungle to cut timber for renovating the house. I want your axe and knife. I'll return it in the evening.'

'To renovate the house?'

'Yes, the house. I mean to extend the roof all around and make a porch on all sides.'

David thought a moment. Then he went silently into the house and brought out an axe and a grass-cutting knife.

'You will have to sharpen that knife on some sand, it's a little blunt.'

'I want a quarter bottle of *kasippu* as well today.'

David gazed at Sadana's face again for a moment as if to discover something. What was written on that face?

'If you have even an eighth left, it is enough.'

David walked down the yard, dragged out a bottle from under a bush and poured a quarter bottle into Sadan's half-bottle. He then gave it to him. Sadana put the bottle to his lips and poured the contents down into his empty stomach, 'Gudus. . . gudus. . . .' David watched in amazement as the *kasippu* went down his throat in two gulps.

Sadana returned the bottle to David and, shouldering the axe and knife, turned to go. He took a few steps, then turned and looked into David's face.

'My woman died last night.' A blazing fire was burning in Sadana's eyes.

David could muster up no words. He stood staring while Sadana quickly stepped over the stile, on to the road and disappeared from sight.

Though he had drunk the *kasippu* in two mouthfuls Sadana did not even clear his throat or spit.

It was quite dark when Sadana returned. All day he had worked. He had dug up some gonawela roots, filled himself with the yams, drunk some water, and so had been able to work without feeling hungry. When he came back to David's house the last of the customers for *kasippu* had already left. He placed the axe and knife against a corner of the porch. The stream of sweat that all afternoon had poured down his ears and coagulated on his body made him stink so strongly that one could barely approach him.

David was not at home. His unprepossessing wife came out. 'Oh dear! It is brother Sadana, is it not? Where on earth have you been? You may not even be able to touch the corpse now. Heavens! What kind of a man are you? With a funeral in your house is this how you set about making the necessary arrangements? Yes, you men! All you want is to smear *kasippu* on your lips. Oh dear, I don't know what has become of the gods that rule the world. But I supposes this is how it is in the dark era of Kali Yug*. Where the devil were you, man? Wandering around with your axe and knife? The menfolk were planning to set off in the morning to comb the forest to find out where you had hung yourself.'

'I went to the forest to work—to cut rafters.'

'Tut tut, enough, enough about what you did. Be off, and get back to your home—even at this late hour. I doubt you'll be in time even to throw a handful of earth on the grave. My children's father went over there this morning—the headman had said that they were to bury the body whether you were there or not, that if a question arose he would answer for it. The father

---

* the last of four eras, it signifies the approaching end of the world and is characterized by a total reversal of all traditional values

of my girls, together with a few other men, made all the arrangements and waited until late this evening hoping you would turn up. But since you didn't come, he's gone to bury her now. Oh dear! Oh dear! Although she was fated by karma to be an invalid, before her illness she was on such good terms with everybody around. It was your drunkenness that caused her death. Otherwise she was not a woman to have died like that. My children's father said they could not keep the corpse even for one more night. It must have been half-decayed even at the moment of death. Off with you now. Go to the graveside anyway, if nothing else.'

Sadana, tying, untying and now knotting the handkerchief round his head, walked with heavy steps, restlessly around the yard. He spoke as soon as David's wife finished her sermon.

'Pour out a half for me.'

'Can you not go without your drink even today?'

Continuing to scold him she poured out half a bottle of *kasippu*. 'Glug, glug, glug, glug.' He finished it in four mouthfuls and stepped down. Then he climbed back on to the porch and approached David's wife. Before she realized what was happening he had snatched the bottle from her hand and drunk the rest of it.

'Thuh!' she spat at him. 'What kind of a man are you?' She began to abuse him. 'It's a good thing for you it is us. For five years you've drunk *kasippu* free of charge. Did you pay a penny for it? Your broken-down house and yard came to us—anybody else would have thrown you out. Do you see? It was because of my children's father that at least your woman could die in her own house. We didn't lay claim to the land, but not because of any consideration for you. It was because of that invalid woman. If we had thrown you out according to the law, she would have long since died in a ditch.'

A lamp was burning inside his house. Sadana, having drunk a full bottle of *kasippu*, came staggering in and sat on a corner of the porch. David stood a long time staring into the yard. 'We buried the body,' he said at last. 'I didn't like to bury her while you were away, but the headman sent some men. . . to wait till evening for you and if you did not come, to bury her. Everybody in the village is grieved at the death. The women of the village brought pieces of white cloth and wrapped the body in it.'

Sadana hiccupped with the *kasippu* now rising to his head. His cheeks puffed up as if he was blowing a conch shell, and 'prssss. . .' they emitted a gust of air.

'This stuff is very strong, man. Looks as if quite a lot grams of *kansa* had fallen into it.'

'I thought you'd blame me for burying the body without you,' said David in a genuinely grieving voice. He was sincerely remorseful and very grieved at the total collapse of Sadana's life.

'I. . . do you know. . . do you know, friend. . . I completed all the work today,' said Sadana, flinging his hands and feet. 'I cut rafters out of good *wira* saplings. For the sticks I cut all *tharana* wood. It will last a hundred years. Yes. I will renovate the whole house, just as we discussed it last night. I will get straw and thatch the roof. Then she will dig up red mud to daub the walls. So everybody will see our house as a proper home. Understand?'

David looked with sorrow at Sadana babbling on drunkenly. 'I am deeply sorry, man, that you have degenerated to this wretched state. That you are so lost,' he said. He looked around as if he could not say what he had intended to say. The half moon that had risęn in the sky was blotted out by a cloud and the darkness deepened. 'I am very sorry, man, but there is nothing more I can do. Yes, nothing I can do. I did all I could. You know well that it is now four-and-a-half years since you mortgaged the house and land and took the money. It was mortgaged for one year only. It has been mine now for over three-and-a-half years. But I didn't say a word about it. This old house is of no use to me, but the land is valuable. You mortgaged it to me for seventy-five rupees but the land is worth much more. That is why I have given you free drinks all these months. If I add up all you've drunk daily, it would amount to over a thousand. But I decided to let it go towards the value of the land. Do you understand, man? Besides, your wife could hardly stand up straight, lying at death's door all this while, and I didn't want, even when the land became mine, to throw a sick woman out. That is why I never mentioned till today that all this belongs to me. I know one shouldn't talk about such matters on a day like this. But since you keep talking about renovating the house, I thought I'd better mention it. Besides, whether we say it today or later, we must, after all, clearly understand these matters. We are also poor people. I'm thinking of clearing this land and planting some coconut trees. You can do some hired work and come and sleep in our house at night. I'm thinking of enlarging the house a little and perhaps renting it to the scavenger coolies who come to work at the hospital. I could get at least ten rupees a month. You understand, don't you? I'm thinking of enlarging the house a little, thatching it with coconut leaves and letting it.'

'No, no, you don't have to use coconut leaves, man,' Sadana, as if he had listened carefully to David's talk, began again to blubber drunkenly. As if throwing up his bellyful of *kasippu*, he continued talking rapidly, 'No, no. You don't have to use coconut leaves. My wife and I are intending to enlarge and renovate the house. We will raise the roof all around, lengthen the rafters and add a porch on all sides. There'll be a porch right round the house and the room in the middle. Then, whether it be a wedding or a work-feast, ten or fifteen people could sit round at one time to eat. That was my woman's idea. All last night we talked about it and decided on it. Ugh! Ugh. . . ! my throat, man! It's amazingly strong, this damned *kasippu* today. But she won't like letting the house. Then where would she sleep when her condition gets bad? Besides, she would certainly not agree to coconut leaves instead of straw. She is a woman who does everything methodically and economically. Why spend unnecessarily on coconut thatch? Straw is more than enough. No need for unnecessary expenditure on damned coconut leaves. Once I extend the house, add the porch and thatch the roof with straw, she will mix the red mud, plaster the walls, redo the floors with dung and rig up the place nicely. Then our house, too, will be a fine house, friend! Then we, too, will have good times. Isn't that right what I'm saying, friend? We, too, will have good times!'

As if trying to banish from his mind the truth which David was trying to bring up, Sadana continued to talk on and on. He vomited forth a torrent of words that seemed to churn up in his throat together with the *kasippu*.

—Translated by Ranjini Obeyesekere

Gunadasa Amerasekera

Disonchinahamy

Kumar Jayawardene, surgeon in-charge of the cancer ward of the State Hospital, lifted his eyes from the microscope and stared impatiently at the glass jar in front of him. It was the tenth time he had done so. Tired of running his eye up and down through the lens of the microscope, Dr Jayawardene turned away angrily and stared at the specimen in the glass jar as if to find some clue that had hitherto eluded him. He stared long and hard, realized that he would find no evidence there and then turned once more to the microscope. It was already four days since the patient's death and he had still not arrived at a correct diagnosis. Did Disonchinahamy die of high blood pressure? Was it 'death due to unforeseen circumstances'? Whichever it was, the doctor was not to blame for it. It was a 'surgical misadventure'.

Jayawardene grabbed the glass jar and turned it upside down, shaking it as if he had a subconscious hunch that something he had not yet seen might suddenly appear there. Each time he turned the jar upside down Disonchinahamy's upper jaw, which was in the formalin solution, swam up to the surface like a tortoise or some live animal. It would rise to the surface instantly as if to provide the answer he was looking for.

Bandusena, Dr Jayawardene's assistant, seated in the far corner of the room reading the Communist party newspaper, lifted his eyes from time to time to watch his boss's actions. Disonchinahamy, whom he had seen and talked to daily during these past two weeks, had now metamorphosed into an upper jaw floating in a glass jar. It aroused in Bandusena a host of questions and irreconcilable feelings; an irrational fury. As several bits of information relating to Disonchinahamy surfaced in his mind, his fury increased. . . . This was the woman who had sat huddled up in bed. . . who had suffered a meaningless death. . . the woman whom the nurses teased because she sat crying all day remembering her home. . . wasn't it? Bandusena felt that there was somewhere, someone, not openly visible, perhaps hidden, but responsible for this death, this fate. . . the answer had to be somewhere. . . . These people called it a surgical misadventure and tried to get out of it but there had to be a cause. . . What damn use was all the research these fellows did. . . ? They strained so hard and discovered what the disease was, the kind of tumour it was, but what good did it do? The hidden thing. . . the fundamental root cause. . . did they find that? . . . Disonchinahamy. . . or if not, Magilinhamy. . . or some Soydahamy. . . their only function was to provide research material so that these fellows could write papers!

Each time Bandusena remembered that he would probably be stuck here till this man finished his work, his anger increased. His organization had its meeting at six-thirty that night. Who knew whether he would be able to get out of here before then?

It was after three in the afternoon, so there was a pervasive silence. There was not a sign of life or movement at this hour of the day in the ward across the corridor. There was not much activity either in the section which admitted patients. Only an occasional patient transferred from a distant hospital entered the Admissions Office.

Jayawardene, who spent the morning in surgery, engaged in operations or examining patients, came to this room in the afternoon to do his research. If he had to spend even a few minutes in administrative chores, Jayawardene considered it an inordinate waste of precious time. As a result, Bandusena, who handled the letters and other business, had also to spend this period in here. It was Bandusena's task, during this time, to read and explain to him the letters, which were mainly in Sinhalese, and to get his signature where necessary. The one administrative task Dr Jayawardene performed was to sign the letters prepared and presented by the meticulously efficient Bandusena.

Thirty-five-year-old Jayawardene was a Fellow of two British surgical associations and a first-class specialist trained in tumour surgery. His father, too, was a well-known medical specialist who had been attached to the main Government Hospital for over twenty years. Kumar obtained his first degree from the Colombo Medical School, left for England and continued to live there for ten years because of his interest and dedication to his field of specialization and research. He had returned to Sri Lanka three years ago, and it was not entirely because of his mother's entreaties.

To the question he constantly asked himself as to what kind of mental attitude he had brought back with him on his return to Sri Lanka, Kumar could give only one answer: that there was within him a deep confusion over and above the sense of isolation. Kumar had known from the outset that, although he had been Senior Registrar at the Hammersmith Post-Graduate Institute for the past eight years, he would not be appointed to a specialist's post for several more years merely because of his 'black' skin. But this fact had become mentally intolerable only quite suddenly. The feeling of being an outsider, a reject of society, which he had been aware of in little ways from the very beginning, began to surface and take a firm grip on his mind only in his fifth year abroad. After that it did not take long for it to grow and spread and become transformed into a permanent mental attitude that would never leave him.

Was it not this attitude that was at the root of the ugly incident that had occurred? Was it not this intolerance which had almost become a mental and physical affliction, that made him catch by the throat the specialist who worked with him and lock him up in a room? Kumar recalled how the investigating committee had recommended he be brought before a psychiatric medical board. The decision to return to Sri Lanka was finally taken in the confusion after that incident. A few days after his return he was appointed Chief Surgeon, in-charge of the cancer ward at the Government Hospital.

Barely six months had passed before Kumar realized that his return to Sri Lanka had been an act of folly. The past three years in Sri Lanka, Kumar now realized, had been spent in a gigantic battle trying to break down and overcome this gradually growing conviction.

If a tumour with a new feature or some new aspect of the disease manifested itself, Kumar seized on it immediately and with great eagerness began his investigations. But how many of these research projects, begun with such enthusiasm, had he abandoned halfway? How unhelpful this poisonous environment was to such research! The absence of a qualified specialist to examine the extent of growth and the ramifications of a tumour meant that he had to do the work of a pathologist too. Where could he obtain the books and journals necessary for such a task? Apart from books and journals, even the instruments necessary for such work could only be found with enormous effort.

More than all this, however, what Kumar could not cope with was the undecided state of his own mind. Six months had not elapsed since his return to his native land before doubts arose as to whether he was not as much an outsider here as in England. As the doubt slowly turned into a conviction he realized that he could not have the peace of mind needed for research. When day-to-day existence in this environment was a hardship, how could he find such peace of mind?

At such moments Kumar felt that if he could at least, with effort, turn his mind on to some research project, he might overcome this sense of isolation and loneliness. It was for this reason that he pursued with such avidity some new tumour or some new manifestation of the disease.

He had resolved to write a paper about the tumour in Disonchinahamy's upper jaw from the very first day that he saw it. For more than a year now he had not written any papers and was not this an excellent opportunity to make a contribution of considerable importance?

Kumar, who had regularly contributed three or four papers a year to the *British Surgical Association Journal*, had, after his return to Sri Lanka, written only three papers. Two of the three were returned with the comment that they had not been well put together. One of the two had some criticisms by his former professor attached to it. One sentence stuck in his mind. 'Your brain seems to be drowsy from the tropical sun. Do you fall a victim to that tropical disease?'

Kumar's reply to that letter seemed an honest confession: 'Returning home was a big mistake. To be treated as an alien in the land of one's birth is a terrible misfortune, is it not? I haven't even the peace of mind necessary for ordinary life, let alone collecting research material for an article. I curse the past I have inherited, and my parents. Last month I quarrelled with my father (reputed to be a doctor, but a man I consider to have earned his living through crookery) and walked out of his enormous house, resolving never to set foot in it again. . . . Sometimes I feel like turning my hand to politics. I feel that only something like politics which binds a man body and soul for twenty-four hours a day can save me from my present calamity, and not research such as this.'

How pleased his professor would be to read this report on Disonchinahamy! Kumar could predict that he would write back immediately asking for all the details of the case. How rarely did one encounter the kind of tumour found on Disonchinahamy! Kumar remembered his professor mentioning that in all of medical literature there were only three accurate reports of this particular tumour which had long been a matter of serious controversy. If so, would not this be the fourth such accurate report? Yet, in preparing the report, how should he approach the matter? This was the big question, the major problem facing him from the moment he sat down to write his report. Should he consider it a 'giant cell granuloma', a 'giant cell tumour' or a 'giant cell sarcoma'? Was this a situation that contradicted the theory that giant cell tumours only occurred in long bones and not in jaw bones? It was not necessary to come to any final decision on this. Nobody expected that. But how good it would be if one could treat it in the report as a giant cell tumour, which all the available evidence seemed to indicate it was. Only then would this case number among the other three accurate reports in medical literature. The chief obstacle about arriving at such a decision, however, was the absence of an accurate case history. If he had been able to speak the Sinhalese language well, might he not have been able to have questioned Disonchinahamy and somehow probe the evidence out of her?

Why had he stopped the Sinhalese lessons so soon in the first year after his return? Had he not given up his large house in Cinnamon Gardens and taken a flat in Borella just in order to learn more about the lives of the ordinary Sinhalese people and the Sinhalese language?

Jayawardene pushed the microscope aside, pulled the four case reports that were lying on the table towards him and began reading them again. 'Come here, Bandusena. . . the diagnosis in this case is now completely up to you. . . . First tell me again the full story the woman gave on that last occasion.'

'What's the use of a diagnosis, sir, after the patient is dead?' Bandusena spluttered, putting aside the newspaper and walking up to him, giving vent to thoughts that had long been festering inside him. Bandusena had been encouraged to treat his boss, Jayawardene, as a friend, by Jayawardene himself. Bandusena recalled how he had even objected at first to being addressed as 'sir'.

'The death of one person does not after all mean the death of medical science. Our responsibility is to science as well as to the patient. One does not encounter a valuable case like this in a hundred years. If we can unravel this case it will be a great service to the entire field. . . . What exactly did that woman say the other night? How many days did she say her face remained blue after being bruised? Each time we asked her a question she would cry. How could we get any answers? I tried so hard to win her confidence but failed. Why do you think that was?'

'What confidence can you expect from that poor destitute, sir? They have no idea what is going to happen to them. They are driven like cattle from hospital to hospital and finally die in some corner. . . . Perhaps she died of sheer terror when she was brought to hospital. All she could say was "yes" and "no" to anything asked.'

'That's a fine thing to say! Why, how considerately we treat our patients here!'

'What good is it that you treat them with consideration? Your kindness is like a drop in the ocean. What use is that. . . ? The woman said her face had remained blue for around two weeks.'

'That's the point I can't accept. She said her face turned blue as a result of her little boy's hand striking her. There's no way a face can turn blue after being hit by a child's hand.' Jayawardene turned to Bandusena and pressed his right hand to his left cheek. 'There's no fat layer here. It's just bone. Only if the bone breaks does a blood clot form. But this bone won't break if a child's hand strikes it. That's the story the woman told us. I asked you to make friends with her and try to get the real story. The bone could break only if it was hit with a ridged implement.'

'I asked her several times when I was writing up her diet chart. But that's all she kept repeating. The moment I tried prying and asking questions about her home she would begin weeping.'

'If only her relatives had come we might have found out.'

'How can they come, sir? They live twenty-three miles away from even the town of Kurunegala. With six children, if they were to come to Colombo for a visit they would probably have to mortgage their house. They may not even own a house to mortgage. I understood from her talk that they lived on a leased-out piece of *hena** land.'

'If in fact the tumour resulted from such a blow then it is undoubtedly a giant cell tumour, not an osteo-sarcoma. There is one theory that giant cell tumours are caused by a serious blow that results in a blood clot. This would be excellent evidence to prove that line of thinking. . . . But not one of these fellows has given a full record of the case. Reading the case reports on Disonchinahamy one gets the feeling that the four reports refer to four different patients. Just read the addresses given here in the four reports.'

Jayawardene took up the first case report—made by the apothecary at the village hospital at Weuda—and handed it to Bandusena. 'Isn't the address on this different from the other one? I find this puzzling.'

Bandusena gazed awhile at both medical records.

'They are both the same. The second one merely states how letters are to be addressed: "To Ukku Banda, c/o Hitchi Mahatmaya at the store by the bridge, 32nd Block, Flower Tree Junction, Weudatenne. . . . " The first one doesn't have a postal address, otherwise they are the same.'

'But the first one doesn't record the fact of any injury to the face. "No history of trauma. . . the face scraped against a wall and was bruised." Then the Kurunegala Hospital record states that a branch of firewood hit her face and that it was swollen for two or three days. It was only here, to us, that she brought up the story that the child's hand struck her. . . . I can't understand it. Besides, it's amazing that for one-and-a-half months, until she was sent here, they did not even perform a biopsy on her. I feel like reporting the whole bunch of them to the Medical Department.'

'What will you achieve by reporting them?'

'Why? Do you think it will have no effect? This kind of shoddy work is a disgrace to the profession. In England they would be expelled from the medical profession. . . . Check how many days she spent in the Weudatenne Hospital.' He handed the charts to Bandusena.

'Eight days at Weudatenne.'

'I suppose one can understand why he kept her for eight days digging needles into her. He was only an apothecary and knew

---

* tract of jungle cleared for shifting cultivation

no better. But how many days did she spend at Karawanella?'

'There she was kept ten days.'

'How many days at the Kurunegala Hospital?'

'Twenty-two days.'

'They kept her for twenty-two days and didn't even think of doing a biopsy! I will not let this pass. I intend reporting every one of them. They are a disgrace to the medical profession. All they did for one-and-a-half months was to drive this woman from one hospital to another. I will report the lot of them.'

'I know what will happen the moment you report them. That wretched apothecary is the only one who will be hit by it. Do you imagine, sir, that the surgeon at Kurunegala will be held to blame? That they will dare to take any action against Dr Gunasinghe? Dr Gunasinghe is married to the Health Minister's niece. The Department knows all about his private practice. I was once attached to the Superintendent of Health Services there, so I know. . . . Dr Gunasinghe never visited the Channel office to examine patients. He was only at the hospital in the mornings. He refused to look at a patient in his ward if the patient had not first consulted him privately in his home and paid him a fee. . . . Do you think the department doesn't know all that. . . ? If you report him, sir, it will still not change anything. That poor fellow, the apothecary, will be made the scapegoat and bear the brunt of it. . . . Look, has Dr Gunasinghe signed this chart at all? He can't even have looked at the poor woman. It's no good reporting him, sir. If our government ever comes to power what we'll do is to line them all up by the nearest wall and shoot the rascals. If one wants to put these things right, sir, one must completely change the system. Bandages or plaster won't do. One must disregard these disgraceful libels on socialism, the kind these fellows indulge in, and change the whole system from its roots.'

'Do you mean to say that when your new socialist society comes into being these things won't occur? Whatever system comes into being, it is still worked by human beings. . . . Have you heard of Kant's saying that it is impossible for this crooked human race to create anything that is not crooked. . . ? Whatever system comes into existence I don't think things will change much. Is there a different system in England? It's the same as this. It's the same kind of democracy, so it's not really the fault of the system, it's the fault of those who work the system.'

Bandusena knew that the frequent political discussions that took place between him and his boss ended inevitably at this point. If he let it go any further he might thoughtlessly come out with certain unnecessary remarks. Bandusena decided therefore that it was better to turn the conversation back on to other lines.

'Disonchinahamy's clothes and other belongings are still in the ward. I reminded you yesterday too, sir, to send them. We should have sent them off the same day to the Medical Superintendent's office. . . . Now it is very late.'

'You should look after such matters. Don't bother me about it.'

'If you don't give the order, sir, the sister won't release them in spite of ten reminders. I'll write a note and send it right now through Ameradasa. Would you sign it?'

Bandusena went to his room, fetched a piece of paper and proceeded to write a note. Meanwhile, Jayawardene continued to compare the medical reports. Bandusena, who had entered the clerical service of the Health Department through the Sinhalese medium, had become Dr Jayawardene's assistant not merely because of the growing regard and liking that had developed between them. There were several other reasons for this friendship. Without Bandusena's help the task of interacting not only with the staff directly under him but also with the patients would undoubtedly have become a serious problem. Dr Jayawardene needed Bandusena's help even to give an order to an attendant working under him. Bandusena noticed that he addressed even an attendant standing in front of him, without looking him in the face. If seven or eight people happened to raise their voices and talk at the same time, he would become alarmed and mentally quite disturbed. If he ever had to approach such a group Bandusena had to be close beside him.

The nickname 'Bashful Maiden' given to Dr Jayawardene by some new attendants seemed very appropriate. Was this bashfulness due to the fact that until quite recently he had not moved around with Sinhalese people? Whatever the reason, Bandusena, who had worked in several hospitals and knew the ways of doctors well, found in Dr Jayawardene a kind of medical man he had not yet encountered. Was it possible that among the tribe of doctors, who were basically heartless murderers and swollen-headed profiteers, someone like Dr Jayawardene could still exist? How could he, who could barely speak Sinhalese, have such a deep concern and care for these poor patients? Bandusena had never known Jayawardene to shout at a patient, or even to raise his voice at them. Was it because he had spent several years studying and working in England that he had developed these fine qualities? Or was it an inherent respect for human beings? Apart from his respect for humanity, why should he treat a Grade III clerk like himself as a friend? Sometimes his very friendliness embarrassed Bandusena, who was not used to such treatment from his superiors. Why had such a kind and good man remained unmarried for so long? Bandusena had not succeeded in finding an answer to this question which bothered him constantly. Did he dislike Sinhalese woman? Or had he remained unmarried because of a thwarted love affair with a white woman? The phrases he would occasionally let slip—'I think all men, except me, are happy'—perhaps implied something of this sort. Bandusena recalled how each time he tried to follow this line of inquiry and peep into Jayawardene's mind to unravel the puzzle of his inner being, it always stopped short at this point.

On one such occasion Bandusesna recalled telling his own history to his boss in order to encourage him to a disclosure.

'Sir, if you feel like that, how should feel? I'm the eldest in my family. The burdens of the entire family rest on my shoulders. . . . My father has been disabled for over a year now. . . . I have four younger sisters. You talk like that, sir, because you have no idea of the sufferings of the poor in this country.'

'Happiness and sorrow are not things one can measure like that, friend. It is not a simple question that your socialist solution can answer.'

That was the answer that he usually gave. Everytime he closed a conversation with that kind of remark, Bandusena realized that however closely he associated with his boss, there was always a certain distance, a great gap between them.

Bandusena began filling up the form for the Medical Superintendent, intending to send it off first thing next morning together with the bundle of clothes. He heard Dr Jayawardene read out aloud a sentence or two of the medical reports he was studying. Watching the intelligent face with its long hair and sharp nose, engaged in deep thought, brought pleasure to Bandusesna. He did not realize that Ameradasa had walked into the room until he saw the bundle of clothes in front of him. He untied the bundle in order to examine it and list the items in the form.

As he opened the bundle and saw the dirty saree wrapped in newspaper Bandusena felt a sharp pang of pain wring his heart. The torn border at the edge had been knotted together in two or three places. Bandusena, gazing at the rag of a saree now taken out of its newspaper wrapping, felt a sharp pain as well as a certain kind of panic or fear. The figure of Disonchinahamy, dressed in that saree and seated on the bed, appeared again in his mind's eye. Had she not sat, just like that, all day in the ward? Seeing him come to endorse her diet chart she would curl herself humbly at the foot of the bed in a pleading manner. At such times was it because of the ugliness of her face and pro-truding left eye that she would look down and hide her face? Was it so as not to show the effluent constantly draining out of her left nostril? Bandusena remembered how her voice would suddenly break and she would collapse into tears in the midst of answering questions even on matters of diet.

Together with the old saree was a battered blouse, two silver bangles wrapped in a piece of paper and a sealed envelope. On it was the address he had read out a while ago. It was written in pencil. Bandusena felt a strong desire to read the contents of this unposted letter. He opened it carefully in such a way that it could be resealed. He read the short letter written in pencil and furtively wiped his eyes with his fingertips. He hurriedly pushed the letter back into its envelope as he felt his eyes begin to dampen again. Stepping out into the corridor, Bandusena paced up and down until the rush of emotion evoked by the letter had subsided. He felt a little ashamed of himself. Return-ing to the room he saw Dr Jayawardene still studying the reports and reading out aloud certain sections of them.

'Age thirty-eight. . . forty-two. . . forty. . . . Age of young-est child. . . three. . . . That's correctly recorded in all three. Eighteen years old at marriage. . . . Bandusena, here, see if you can make sense of this. . . . The descriptions given in these records are all different from each other. Only the apothecary out of the lot of them has even attempted to get a good case history. Read this again and see how correct my notes are.'

Bandusena began reading the record of the apothecary. He was interrupted from time to time by Dr Jayawardene who stopped to include facts he had forgotten in his report.

'Name: Ilindu Kankanamge Disonchinahamy. . . . Age: thirty-eight. . . . Employment: Daily paid labourer. . . . Married. . . Husband, labourer. . . . Number of chidren: six, eldest died. Present eldest child, female, age thirteen years. . . . Youngest child, age three years. . . . General health: satisfactory. Face and hands and feet show a certain pallor. Endemic malnutrition suspected. A year ago, because of excessive fatigue and panting, stopped work on weeding of the upper section of the hill. No serious illness prior to this. . . .'

Bandusena, startled, stopped reading the medical record. He heard a great wailing noise from the direction of the ward. What could be the cause of this weeping and wailing coming from that direction at this time of day? Dr Jayawardene, too, strained his ears to listen.

Bandusena went out of the room to inquire. He saw Ameradasa coming down the corridor with a man dressed in a sarong and shirt, who was holding his head in his hands and weeping loudly.The man suddenly flung himself, sprawling, beside the open door, and like one who had lost all consciousness of the world around him, held his head and wept even more loudly than before. 'Aney. . . good sir, I can't bear this any longer. Aney. . . Buddha-like good sir. . . who would have thought this possible. . . not even in my wildest dreams. . . . Good sir, why didn't you tell me. . . ? I cannot bear it. . . .'

Dr Jayawardene had much difficulty in disengaging himself from the grasp of the man who sprawled on the floor embracing his feet.

'It's Disonchinahamy's husband. He has only just received the telegram and here he is. . . . Only the first telegram we sent him reached him, not the second one,' Ameradasa whispered in Bandusena's ear.

The man sprawled at the door held his head with his hands and wailed like an animal. Bandusena and Dr Jayawardene looked at each other, not knowing what to do. Bandusena shouted at the crowd following him down the corridor, and told them to leave. He took the man sprawled on the floor by the hand and spoke to him, trying to lead him into the room. The man flung Bandusena's hands aside, weeping and wailing with an upturned face like that of a toothless buffalo, unable to control himself.

'Let him be till the hysterical spell passes,' said Dr Jayawardene, moving a little away and whispering in Bandusena's ear. Till then he had stood stock still, not knowing how to handle the situation.

Bandusena had been told to shut the door each time he came into the doctor's office, and yet why had he still not got used to this habit? This kind of intrusion was the price one paid for not doing so. Would this man stick around the room for the next two or three hours?

'Alas. . . good sir. . . where am I to go? With five young ones on my hands where on earth can I go. . . ? If I could only end my own life here, now. . . . It would all be over then. . . kind sir. . . this was all my fault. It happened because of me. . . . I saw the little one crying of hunger and couldn't bear it. . . . I threw the plate I had in my hand at her. That was what caused it to swell up. . . sir. . . kind sir. . . what am I to do?'

Bandusena took him firmly by the hand and forced him to a corner of the room in order to explain to him all that had happened and to try and console the man. But the man lay down again on the floor beside the chair that was placed for him, banged his head against it and continued to weep and wail.

'Alas, good sir. . . if I could only have given her just one spoonful of medicine. . . if I could have done some little act of caring for her in her sickness. . . . When I arrived at the Karawanella Hospital they said she had been sent to Kurunegala. When I went to Kurunegala they said she had been sent here. . . . Kind sir, I pawned our rice ration books to make this journey. . . . '

Instead of listening to Bandusena struggling to explain the position, the man continued with his own lamentations.

'Sir. . . How am I to take her away. . . ? What else can I do but stand here and watch you do what you wish with her. . . . I pawned our rice-ration books to make this journey.' When he was not speaking he would just clasp his head in both hands and wail. 'Kind sir, what can I do with my five children?'

In the midst of all this weeping, wailing and lamenting, Bandusena tried to make certain facts clear to him and finally got him to go with him and Ameradasa to the hospital mortuary to see the body of Disonchinahamy. After walking a little distance in the direction of the mortuary Bandusena asked Ameradasa to stay with the man, and he came back to the office himself, knowing that he could not bear to look at such a searing scene.

On his return he was amazed to see Dr Jayawardene once again absorbed in his microscope and back at work as if nothing had happened. He was not even aware of Bandusena's return. Bandusena sat down in his chair trying to recall what had happened, like a man awakening from a terrible dream and desperately trying to regain his wits. Dr Jayawardene, engaged in his work and silent for a long while, finally spoke.

'What do you think of my guess? Dead right, wasn't it?' Jayawaradene asked, turning to Bandusena.

'What are you talking about, sir?' Bandusena replied, completely at sea.

'Didn't you hear him? That man said the initial injury that caused the wound was a result of him hitting her with a plate.

'Is that so. . . ? I can't remember his saying that. . . .'

'That is what is meant by saying that a doctor's ears and eyes are different from those of ordinary people. If that woman had given us just that little bit of information we could have come to a definite diagnosis right away. This is a giant cell tumour. Why did the woman lie, instead of speaking the truth from the very beginning?'

'That's natural. They may be poor but they are people with a sense of dignity. Village folk are like that. . . . It's only women from these towns who go complaining to the police and in the law courts that their husbands have hit them. Women in the village may be poor but they would consider that uncivilized.'

'What is civilized or uncivilized here?' Jayawardene spoke with a half-smile. 'Is it civilized to throw a plate at one's wife? It seems to me anyway, from the way he gets into fits of temper and his excessive emotionalism, that the man is more like an animal in his reactions and instincts. . . anyway. . . I shall probably never in my life find a case-history quite like this. This is a report that will make medical history.'

Dr Jayawaradene abruptly stopped speaking and ran towards the microscope, suddenly recalling something. He should be able to find confirmation for it in the slide. How true it is that the eyes see only what the mind has already seen. How had he failed to observe till now this characteristic, so clearly visible in all the slides? Dr Jayawardene began tapping the table with his fingertips in his satisfaction.

'Disonchinahamy will undoubtedly enter into medical history. I don't think a case like this has ever been reported. . . . The

Case of Disonchinahamy, Reported from Sri Lanka. . . . '

'What good will it do that destitute, sir, whose corpse cannot even be taken home for a decent burial, that she is entered in the annals of medical history?' asked Bandusena, unable any longer to control the impatience seething inside him.

'Those are not my problems.'

'They may not be your problems, sir, but they are vital questions. . . . All these questions have just one answer. Until we get that answer, whatever anyone does will be no good.' Bandusena spoke in a voice slightly more shrill than before.

'Even if you get your answers I don't think these things will improve. . . . Problems such as these don't have such short and simple answers.'

'Short or long, sir, there is still only one answer. You don't have these problems, sir, so you don't see the need for answers to them. But destitutes like us need answers. . . . If you can understand Sinhalese, sir, you had better read the letter the poor woman wrote just before she died. Here, let me read it for you since you probably can't: "When I came here from Kurunegala Hospital I implored the nurse to send you a telegram. Did you get it. . . ? I am now in Colombo Hospital, Ward 33. We were brought here in an ambulance. I wait anxiously for you to come. I have given my consent to the operation because it is necessary to get this cured as soon as possible and get back home. . . . If I die you will have to bring up the little ones. I keep remembering our small son's face. Does he still ask, When is mother coming home? When I think of him my heart is about to burst. If I die, look after my little ones. Mr Hitchi has still to pay us for two bunches of bananas. Ask Mr Hitchi to lend you what money you need for travelling. I have still to get three days' wages for the weeding. . . . Don't be upset. The operation is tomorrow. They look after me well. The doctors constantly see to me. May the Buddha's protection be with you and the children." ' Bandusena read the closing sentences of the letter in a breaking voice. Dr Jayawardene said nothing, but he, too, sensed the turmoil in Bandusena. Bandusena's eyes were wet with tears. Why was he so moved by the contents of that letter?

Dr Jayawardene's silence increased rather than decreased Bandusena's agitation and turmoil. 'It's a good thing for you, sir, that you don't understand the Sinhalese language. . . . You are just like our present socialist leaders who can't speak it. Is it surprising that they can't see our sufferings?'

'Still, my friend, how can you find simple solutions to these problems?'

'Simple or not, these are wrongs that this world cannot bear for much longer. That's all I know. . . . These are wrongs that the world will not bear for much longer.'

Bandusena walked towards his table, glancing with seething anger and repulsion at Dr Jayawardene who was back again with his eye glued to the microscope. He wanted to fling the damned microscope and all that damned research material out of the window. Destitutes come and fall at the feet of these men like flies or mosquitoes and die. . . . their research. . . that was all that mattered. . . . He, too, was like all that other lot. . . the same philosophy was ingrained in him. . . . The only difference was that he disguised it. . . .

Bandusena who was seated stood up suddenly. 'Sir, when you finish, lock the door and leave the key with the watcher. I have all the other keys with me,' he said, walking out to the room.

Deep in thought, Dr Jayawardene seemed not to have heard him. Stepping out on to the road Bandusena did not wait for a bus but continued to walk, his mind distorted with emotion that would not allow him to stand still. As he walked, he stared in front of him and muttered to himself like a madman.

Two weeks later Dr Jayawardene walked into the dissecting room of the medical school with an enthusiasm that had been building up in his mind all through the previous night. Before that enthusiasm faded or died he resolved firmly to garner the few remaining facts necessary for writing up his case. As a result of the overpowering sense of despair and ennui that had suddenly come over him last week, he had thrown the first draft of his article aside, and had now found it only after a great deal of searching.

If he was to complete his piece of research he had to dissect and examine several more parts of Disonchinahamy's body. It was difficult to find Disonchinahamy's body amidst the collection of bodies flung on the stone slabs of the dissecting room. He finally located it by examining the tags hung around the necks of the bodies. He found Disonchinahamy's right arm cut off from the body. A medical student was fondly handling it, searching among the muscles for a certain cluster of nerves. Three other students, standing at the other end, poked around in her head and face. Dr Jayawardene needed only parts of the liver and spleen. Seeing that particular part of the body untouched, he was quite content.

—*Translated by Ranjini Obeyesekere*

Gunadasa Amerasekera

Darkness That Calls Forth Demons

Over the roofs, shrouding the houses, darkness spreads
Veils I had drawn now rip apart, demon faces peer.
Desolate windows of my mind which I kept tightly shut,
　　burst open
Sleeping demon faces freshly revived, awaken.

Their footsteps clatter noisily as they rush about our yard
They chase each other around and around and surround the
　　house
They peer in at the window, hurl blood-curdling shrieks and
　　yells
They are trying to get in at the door, where shall I hide
　　myself?

They kick the door again and again, demand I open it.
They squeeze each other by the throat, scream with death-
　　like shrieks.
They hoot three hoots three times in succession, leer through
　　the window-pane
There's no escape for me now, where shall I hide myself?

'Why do you shut your door and lie huddled up, idiot?
We want to eat your bloody flesh, open up this minute.'
They yell at the top of their voices, peer, leering at my
　　window
There—they rush in through the battered door, where can I
　　hide myself?

A thousand demons from my past all around me cluster
They burst in through the busted door, demand to eat my
  liver.
I dare not stay, these demons demand sacrificial offerings
Quick, tell me some place to escape to, at this moment when
  darkness is falling.

My own imaginings I know take life and appear as demons
To chase them out or beat them down, I have not the power
  or knowledge.
At the moment of gathering darkness they come crowding
  and envelop me;
Quick, tell me of a place that is safe and to that haven take
  me.

—Translated by Ranjini Obeyesekere

Siri Gunasinghe

Dirty Dishwater

Man's mind is a kitchen
Learning, it's dishwater.
I grovel, lapping it up.

Black crows flock
to drive me away
It is not easy to escape.

Dishwater stagnates in the drain
with stale leftovers
scraped off broken plates.

No salt or flavour in it
nothing to fill one up.

Hurt by a hurled coconut shell
leg-lifted
yelping
I still cannot tear myself away
from that drain.

All that gave life
to a lifeless existence—
dishwater
The only flavour
in a flavourless life—
stale food.

—Translated by Ranjini Obeyesekere

Mahagama Sekera

Moon and New York City

Only the cement walls,
Blackened, and competitively rising.
No sky, no greenery.
In New York City
At the topmost floor
Of the one-hundred-storeyed building
I am imprisoned in a room
With doors and windows all closed,
A bed, a chair, a table
And me.

I think
Of my beloved parents,
Friends and relatives, wife and children
On the other side of the earth.
To dispel the loneliness
I recite a poem aloud.
My voice comes ringing
Back to my ears,
Not knowing where to go.

I open the window and look out,
I look far down below.
The invading cold
Pierces my face.

Caught in the glare of neon lights
Vehicles speed along
Lacking any patience,

Ant-like human machines
Dart in all directions.
There is no one here
Who would pause for a moment
To look at me kindly,
To exchange a few words with me.
Such persons are all
On the other side of the earth.
I think of them.

I look up sadly.
Shining brightly in the sky
Like a plate of gold—
The moon.
The moon that I know so well,
The moon that sparkles on the fields at home,
The moon that sparkles on the temple sand.

—Translated by Wimal Dissanayake

Thilakaratna Kuruvita Bandara

Premadasa—Pity and Rage

The morning sun
flings its rays of heated iron spikes,
pricks me awake,
drives me to the office.

The swing doors of the office
gape, gulp me down.

Inside that dreary graveyard
the day slowly withers away.

When, saddened by the dying sun
dark clouds drift in a procession
the mouth of the office opens wide
like a poisonous spider
who sucks the living essence and
spews out the corpse,
releases us.

How can I return again to that dreary empty room?

Somewhere, in some theatre
in some way pass the time.
If there's a show on—well and good—
if not, a rehearsal will do.
If all the halls are empty
I'll go find a friend and talk.

Eight o'clock is too early yet to return to the room.

If I don't meet a drinking companion,
drift alone to a familiar bar.

The waiter comes towards me like a lover,
'Why, sir, do you drink so much?
I would allow you only a dram.
It's not good for you, sir, to drink so much. . . .'
Attending at the other table
where two lovers sit
murmuring sweet love talk,
Premadasa turns on me,
eyes, compassion-damp.
I see, that look.
Instantly
a burning desire
to kick the table
smash it
rise, and flee,
overcomes me.

—Translated by Ranjini Obeyesekere

Monica Ruwanpathirana

Piyasena's Question

The Christmas Vacation had ended when I first came here
I was brought to walk to the city school with the little master.
I'd already finished all the sums with seven and eight times
  tables
I'd read the stories in my book, completed all the lessons.
I had recited all the poems about the cat and squirrel
And when I left my village school I'd passed the second level.

I'd walk to school each morning holding little master by the
  hand
And every evening we'd walk home, always hand in hand.
I'd sit outside his schoolroom, upon the short stone wall
The stories told by the teachers, from there I'd hear them all.
Chanting verses, holding hands we'd sit at dusk, the two of
  us
The story of Prince Gemunu, we'd learn, the two to us.

But though that's so, there's one thing more that I can't
  figure out
Would one of you find out for me and kindly let me know.
Little master who was in third grade has now passed to the
  fourth
I, too, was in the same third grade, when will I get to
  fourth?

—*Translated by Ranjini Obeyesekere*

Wimal Dissanayake

A Poem on the Moon

Within the darkening forest groves their three loud hooting
  'halloos' ring
Their footstep strike Earth's heart and bring a troubling
  terror as they bound;
With hands linked, in a narrowing ring, whirling they wheel
  and hem me round
To sear my living flesh to ash with the red sparks their
  eyeballs fling—

Hands reaching out to grasp my throat, demanding blood,
  they throng agape:
No hope of fleeing from this doom—I see that there is no
  escape;
Why grieve then since no hope remains? Knowing what I
  must suffer soon
I fix my eyes upon the sky to see the splendour of the moon.

—Translated by Lakshmi de Silva

Parakrama Kodituwakku

Court Inquiry of a Revolutionary

I. (School Report)

Doubts all teachings.
Questions continuously.
Thinks individualistically.
Disregards discipline.
Works as he chooses.
Conduct unsatisfactory.

II. (Religious Instructor's Report)

Disbelief verily, signifieth a sinful mind.
The horoscope too indicateth a lack of merit.
Choleric humours have become excited, turbulent.
Hath no knowledge of the doctrine of the gods.
I take refuge in the Buddha. He should do so too.

III. (Court Report)

(a) Attempted to break the law.
(b) Destroyed the peace.
(c) Should be ordered a whipping.
(d) Be made into a good citizen.

IV. (Doctor's Report)

Sick.
Psychiatric treatment advised.

Phobia, mania, paranoia, hysteria,
Neurotic, psychotic,
Abnormal—criminal
Behaviour unnatural.

Brain surgery recommended
Demonic fantasies to be controlled,
Before going to bed
Several tablets of phenobarbitone.

V. (Statement of the Accused)

Turn me not into a snail
my feelers chopped off.
Turn me not into a coward
by preaching of gods.
Turn me not into a buffalo
burdened with false views.
Make me not a 'good boy'
with hands and mouth gagged.

Allow me to question like Socrates
Doubt like Descartes
Crash through like a gushing river
cut clean as a knife.
Let me rise, erect
Like a penis.

—*Translated by Ranjini Obeyesekere*

Parakrama Kodituwakku

An Unfinished Lesson

One by one each burnt-out leaf
falls, fills the yard.
A blackbird cries a sharp 'tu. . . week'
perched upon a mound.

Blackbird, is that a question
you too ask of me
because you know me for a schoolteacher?

A full half of my life I've spent
answering questions.
Now my white-haired head
has no more strength.

Those who asked me questions then
where are they now?
To questions that are posed to them
what answers do they give?

Children, you who walked to school by flowering forest trails,
You who brought the clouds with you, down mountain
    slopes,
You who stepped through cool stream beds to wash your feet,
Tell, o tell, where are you now, in what far place?

There was no playground for the school,
you trained on the bus route,
The hundred metres race was run
on the scorching road, barefoot,

While I stood at the bend, alert
for passing cars.

Where are you now, the lot of you?
whether far or near
Raise your hand for me to see
and answer clearly 'here'.

. . . Do you still, now, as you did then,
get drenched in the pouring rain,
trapped in the threatening storms,
wade across rushing streams,
see laughter in the sun,
run races on the road
see a winning post ahead?

A full half of my life I've spent,
answering ·questions
Now my white-haired head
has no more strength.

—Translated by Ranjini Obeyesekere

Part III

Writing in Tamil

P. Thambirajah

Funeral Pyre

Most of you may not know Moopan Sinnavian. But everyone in our village, from the schoolboy up to the village elder with one foot in the grave, knew him.

He was neither a distinguished political personage nor one of those heroic Tamils ready to sacrifice their lives for their language. But he was descended from the same heroic stock as these. He did not understand the intricacies either of politics or language. His ancestors, it seems, once sounded the battle drums, arrayed in the front line of the fray. Their descendants, today, were required to beat the tom-tom at funerals. This was the command of the important personages of our village.

Sinnavian was the leader of the band of tom-tom beaters. I never heard anyone address him as Sinnavian. In his presence, they called him Moopan. Among themselves, they referred to him, behind his back, as 'that pariah'.

His body was thin and bent; he looked older than he really was. Irregular patches of stubble sprouted here and there, like coarse grass, on his unshaven face. His hair was gathered behind in a knot. The ingrained, obsequious habit of thrusting his shawl under his armpit and bowing respectfully to anyone passing along the road had hunched his body. His yellowing, soiled *veshti** was tied above his knees. Such was the appearance that fifty-year-old Moopan Sinnavian presented.

Moopan's hut was at the top of the lane leading to the cremation ground. It stood on a mound in a heath. Close by was a palmyra grove; beyond that could be seen the *smashan*** which fed alike on high caste and Harijan.

---

* the unstitched white lower garment of Tamil men, worn from midriff to ankle; ** a place where corpses are cremated or buried

Moopan was born to slave for our village. Not one day had he lived for himself. His conjugal life had been brief. Ponni, his beloved wife, possessed a mind like washed Chinese rice. For three years she caused no end of anxiety to Sinnavian. Alas, one day as she was gathering the fallen, dry leaves in the palmyra grove, she was bitten by a snake. Moopan made several vows. A magician was summoned, but all to no avail. Shuddering in every limb, the pregnant woman passed away.

Sinnavian felt that his own life had ended. Innumerable corpses had he cremated or buried; yet he could not bear to think of Ponni's death.

With his own hands he buried Ponni's corpse in the *smashan*. Standing over the grave, he sobbed like a child. His disciples, Sinnappan and Seenian, forcibly led him back to his hut. He had not a wink of sleep that night. At midnight he crept back to the *smashan* and, standing over Ponni's grave, cried his heart out. When the cock crowed at dawn, he turned back and walked along the lane. Suddenly his foot struck against something: he kicked it aside. Whimpering, a puppy lay sprawled on the ground.

Sorrow sympathized with sorrow. He picked the little creature up: it was a bitch. Someone, not wishing to rear a bitch, had abandoned it. Tenderly, he stroked its head; it wagged its tail. Fondling it, he walked towards his hut. The animal irresistibly commanded his attention. Love which had been so cruelly snatched away from him, grew again in another form.

Time passed and the puppy grew up. Moopan's body was gradually wasting away. Yet he reigned supreme as tom-tom beater. Standing on the melting tar, as the funeral procession wended its way to the road junction, Moopan would vigorously beat his drum in an unanswerable challenge to his disciples. It was then that one realized his superb artistry.

Sinnappan and Seenian, his disciples, were the only ones who intimately knew and appreciated Moopan's skill and the integrity of his life. The sight of Moopan, Sinnappan, Seenian and the dog on the street, would provoke only one question: 'Who's dead, Moopan?'

Moopan, hugging the tom-tom slung over his shoulder close to his body, would cower like a beaten dog as he replied with bowed head. His voice would then shake with emotion.

As loud lamentations and cries filled the funeral house, Moopan's suppressed sorrow would reveal itself in his cadences.

Sometimes, he would remember his wife Ponni. Then, unconsciously, tears would well into his eyes, trickle down his parched cheeks and disappear amidst the grass-like stubble on his face.

'Master is dead, how lucky, how lucky. . . ! A few coins for me, for me. . . !' Unsympathetic people would sarcastically remark that this was the rhythm Moopan beat out. Death would mean a full stomach for him that day, they would say. Small wonder he was overjoyed at the prospect!

Tom-tom beating was not all he had to do. Sometimes the carcass of a stray dog or cat would lie rotting in the street while passers-by held their noses against the overpowering stench. It was Moopan who buried the putrid flesh. He was also summoned to bury the carcasses of dead cattle and goats. If he performed these duties for the chairman of the local council, he was given a few coins. That was all.

You could hear Moopan's tom-tom on festival days at Vairavar Kovil and even at Amman Kovil. On these days, milk, rice and plantains were freely given to him. Such was his fee.

Like so many others, Moopan possessed one secret desire. This was neither for money nor for the privileged life of the high castes. His desire revolved round his own death. His disciples should beat their tom-toms at his funeral; accompanied by tom-tom beating, his friends should lay his body on the stacked pile of wood and set fire to it. That was all he desired—a small desire, surely.

'Sinnappan, when I die you will succeed me. But one thing I want of you: at my funeral, you must display all your skill,' Moopan would often say.

'Where else can we display it, if not at your funeral?' his disciple would reply.

It was the day of the festival at Nallur Kandaswamy Kovil. Moopan too had gone there. It was one bustling, jostling mass of humanity. Moopan flinched from contact with the others, but he could not help brushing against them. He was an untouchable: this was engraved deeply in his consciousness. Unable to stay there any longer, he walked back to his village.

The moon shone resplendently. Moopan remembered a night when Ponni had accompanied him to the festival. Laden with a new mat and boxes, they had walked back home, munching gram. Immersed in these reminiscences he was now walking on, forgetful of himself. Suddenly he heard a noise behind him. A speeding bullock-cart was bearing down upon him. Before he could step out of the way, he was knocked down by the yoke. The wheel ran over his shoulder.

'*Aiyo*, Master!' came the choking cry. The bullock-cart slowed down and someone turned to look.

'Wretched drunken cur! Stay at home instead of staggering about on the streets,' roared one of the men, but Moopan did not hear him.

'Urge the bullocks forward,' ordered the other. They trundled away into the distance.

How long Moopan lay in the street is not known. When he regained consciousness, day had dawned. He realized that he was lying in his hut. His whole body was aching and he could not turn.

'Seeni, Seeni,' he groaned.

'I have rubbed in oil. The pain will soon disappear,' Seenian comforted him.

Sinnappan and Seenian did all they could, but it was of no use. The hands, which had worked ceaselessly for the village dead, beating subtle cadences on the tom-tom, became stiff and motionless.

The dog which Moopan had reared trotted round and round the corpse, wagging its tail. It licked his legs. Often it howled dismally as it lay curled up at the feet of the corpse.

The lamentations and cries of the women in the neighbourhood rent the air.

After they had stacked the logs of wood in the crematorium, Sinnappan and Seenian returned to the hut. Along with their disciples, they started drumming. It satisfied them enormously to pay their last respects to their guru.

The tom-toms were heard to the farthest corner of the village.

'Who is dead? Who's dead?' This was the question on everyone's lips.

'Moopan Sinnavian,' replied a boy who was passing the junction. No one believed him.

'An unheard-of practice! What, tom-toms at a pariah's funeral?' growled someone doubtfully.

'I hear they have already set up the pyre. They are going to cremate Sinnavian, it seems,' said someone else.

'A new-fangled practice! What audacity!'

'We must teach these pariahs a good lesson!'

'Let's go!'

The mob set out from the junction, incensed with rage—as if their honour had been violated.

'What has happened? Where are you all going?' demanded people on the way.

'Haven't you heard. . . ? Tom-toms and a funeral pyre for Moopan!' The ranks of the mob swelled, as it advanced.

'You there, stop that!' roared one of the leaders.

Suddenly, the drums fell silent. The bewildered drummers hurriedly rose and bowed respectfully.

'Who told you to beat the tom-toms?'

'Moopan asked us to. . . Master,' replied Sinnappan.

'So?'

'Sinnavian was our guru, Master. That is why. . . !'

'So, tomorrow you'll ask for the hands of our daughters, if he tells you to, isn't it?'

'No, Master. Please don't say that. Can't we pay our last respects to our guru, Master?'

'How dare you argue with me? What infernal cheek!' He swung the stick he held in his hand. The blow crashed on Sinnappan's face.

Sinnappan collapsed on the ground, calling for his mother who had died ten years before.

In a few minutes, the high caste men assembled there were transformed into raging brutes.

The drums were broken; the drummers were assaulted. The pariah women fled for their lives.

The dog began to bark furiously; it even attempted to bite. A stone was hurled at it. Limping, it ran inside.

The mob crowed over its victory. An ingenious idea flashed into someone's mind. He set fire to Moopan's hut. Tongues of flame leaped up and licked at the old timbers. Blazing wood and embers fell on Moopan's corpse.

Drunk with victory, the mob turned back.

With aching hearts and bodies, Sinnappan and Seenian stood watching their guru's corpse being burnt to ashes.

Early next morning, both of them cast the charred bones into the sea off Keerimalai.

—*Translated by A.J. Canagaratna*

K. Saddanathan

Vimala

No sooner did she receive the urgent telegram than she decided to leave for the village. These was not time even to rush to her flat. She proceeded from the office to the Fort railway station in time to catch the noon train to Jaffna.

Siva, her assistant, had wanted to go along as her escort. But then it dawned on them that both were expected to attend a staff conference in the Ministry of Labour in two days time. Now that she was going away, at least he would have to be present.

The air-conditioned car had no vacant seats, and she had to be content with a second-class seat. It was uncomfortable all right, but does one look for comfort at a time like this. . . ? It was an urgent telegram, after all.

Why this mighty hurry? Her father, who had sent the telegram, was always in a hurry.

After a lapse of almost eight months she was going to her village—to return, to be engulfed in the anxieties of her home, to sink into despair. It was much better to be in Colombo, to be cut off, free, alienated.

The friendship she had established with Siva—the young man's intelligence, had given to her life a certain fullness. To have similar tastes and ideas is not a common thing. She liked Ray's films. But for him it was not merely Satyajit Ray; he would go on enumerating all the giants of the film world. She would listen fascinated.

If the conversation drifted into literature or art, then he would really be in his element. He could speak with equal authority on painting, fiction, or modern poetry. It was he who had introduced Henry James, Joyce and Gorky to her. She now loved to read Gorky.

Their relationship was a result of their common tastes and

background. Beyond that, it was difficult to be sure. As far as she was concerned he was a mere boy. Hardly twenty-two. She often marvelled, however, at the maturity he revealed.

Siva was not really conscious that Vimala was thirty. Her face was oval, and the eyes wide. Compassion seemed to seep through them. Her hair flowed in waves to her ankles. Tall and slim, she was beautiful. He could not dispel her image from his mind. He once asked her, 'Vimala, with all your beauty, why do you remain single?'

'Ah, marriage. You think looks alone will secure that?'

With a mirthless laugh she stood gazing at something. Her eyes glistened. After that he never broached the topic for fear of causing her pain.

There was no one to meet her at the Jaffna railway station. True, she had not sent a message, but couldn't someone have come on the off chance that she might arrive?

She got into a taxi and reached home. The silence that engulfed her home was broken occasionally by the sound of her mother's moans. As she entered the house, her younger sister Ranji rushed up and embraced her.

'Mother, Sister has arrived.'

Vimala looked at Ranji. Her eyes were swollen. She had been crying. Father was not around. She crossed the hall and entered a room. 'Ranji, get me a dressing gown—I'm coming straight from the office.'

She hastily removed the saree, tossed it away, and reached for the dressing-gown. In a corner, Susi, Rani and Saki—three other sisters—lay fast asleep, their legs flung carelessly over each other. These three were born after Indhu, another sister.

'Ranji, why are the children heaped like this? Can't there be some kind of order?'

'What kind of order can there be here, Sister. Everything is in a mess.'

'What did you say?'

Father was heard spitting noisily outside.

'Father has returned. He went to Uncle's place.'

By the time Vimala changed and came to the veranda, her parents, Saras and Indhu were already there. Saras was born before Indhu. Only her second sister, Chithra, was not around.

'Where has Chithra gone?' Vimala asked.

'Chithra. . . ?' Mother broke down. It was pathetic to watch her whole frame shake with sobs.

Father now spoke. 'That wretch has run away with that Indian servant Velauthan who was working at Thillai's place.'

He too broke down.

She could hardly believe her ears. How could she possibly believe this? She looked up and glanced directly at Indhu and Saras. They got up and went into the house. It was at this point that they heard the gate being closed.

'Who is it?' Father called out.

'It's me.'

Uncle and his son, Shanmugam, entered. Ranji went in and brought a chair for Uncle. He sat down wearily and said, 'Look here. . . this has made us hang our heads in shame. I too have daughters. Your other uncle and his brother, Pasupati, have two daughters each. As for your father, all his offspring are daughters. Now is it possible to give them in marriage? That girl has brought shame on all of us. I never thought she would run away with an Indian. Our family, after all, is not to be sneered at. You have to only mention that we are from Thavadi, and who will refuse a proposal. They will fall over each other to give their sons. This mad girl has rushed things. Look here, Vimala, you are thirty. Aren't you still waiting? What has to happen will happen all in good time. But for that reason one does not do something abominable like this. What are you going to do about this? You can't ignore it, can you? We can make an entry, but Shanmugam says that since she is of age, the police are powerless. Maybe he is right. We can't drag all this muck to the police station.'

'No, we can't go to the police. I think we ought to make a trip to Periyakanam. It's only a mile away from Kilinochchi. That's where Velauthan's parents live.'

'Is that so? Then, first thing in the morning, go there. If she is there, drag her back. This must be done with the utmost secrecy. No one knows this in the village. Either we bring her back before the village gets scent of it, or we have to hide our faces.'

Having said this, the two of them stepped down from the veranda and moved away.

'Vimala, how many days leave have you applied for?' Father asked.

'I can't stay long, Father. I must go back tomorrow. There is a meeting with the minister on the day after.'

'Tomorrow? Without seeing this to an end?'

'What can we do about it? She has made her decision.' Having flung these words, Vimala addressed Ranji.

'Get a lantern, bring some soap, and come with me to the well.' As her sister drew the water and handed it to her, she poured it on her head.

'What's this, Sister? You pour water on your head at this hour of the night?'

'I want to wash out this whole family. I can't. Can't I at least throw some water on my head?'

Ranji stood by aghast. Her vision blurred as tears rolled down.

'Ranji, don't cry. This is why I prefer to be in Colombo. I can't shoulder this burden any more. To take only what I need from my salary, send home the rest, and to remain in Colombo is far more satisfying. Is it enough if they simply bear children? Is there no obligation to give them in marriage? If they don't do it, then Chithra is not to be blamed. Even I may do it. They brag about their prestige. They are of the reputed Vellala* caste, aren't they? People will fall over each other to give their sons. The only thing is no one has done it yet. What's my age, and what's yours? What's the age of our eldest cousin? Are we not all becoming old maids?' She spoke with bitterness.

Ranji was taken aback. She had never seen her sister like this. She was one who would shrug off anything. But now. . . .

Ranji made her sit down and poured the water on her sister's head. Won't this water cool that smouldering heart? She yearned to know.

Vimala's fit of anger subsided, and she asked, 'What's wrong with Mother, Ranji? She doesn't look too well.'

'Yes, Sister, the baby is due soon.'

'What? Have they still not exhausted their lust? Chithra is young. What's the harm if she runs away. I'll go to Kilinochchi tomorrow, tell her that what she did was perfectly right and go on to Colombo.'

'Kandasamy, the astrologer, says that it will be a boy this time.'

'I see. A boy to seek the dowry for his eight sisters, eh?'**

---

* the farmer caste which in Jaffna is considered the highest caste; ** it is customary in Jaffna, that a son, when he marries, gets a dowry from the bride's family, which is in turn often used by his family to give as dowry for his sister to marry

'Sister, please try not to shout.'

'Why, why shouldn't I shout?'

'She's hysterical all right,' Ranji muttered.

Vimala changed, went into a room, shut the door, and fastened the bolt. Ranji banged on the door twice. These was no reply.

'Poor Sister, she didn't even have something to drink,' Ranji thought as she walked quietly away and lay down beside her mother.

She woke up with a start.

'Ranji. . . Ranji,' she heard the whisper and gently slipped out of the house.

'Shall we go into the garden?'

'No. . . please.' She feigned reluctance.

Shanmugam and Vimala boarded the Mullaitivu bus. The girl is scared of Vimala, so let Vimala go with Shanmugam and talk to her. This was the considered opinion of the elders. The bus stopped at Kilinochchi, and both of them alighted.

'Shall we hire a car?' Shanmugam asked.

'No, it's only a mile. Let's walk,' she said. They walked along a rutted lane.

'Incidentally, there is something I want to tell you. . . in fact, I want you to be the first one to know it,' said Shanmugam. His face appeared a little flushed. She looked at him in astonishment. 'You know, Vimala, I like Ranji a lot. She too likes me. It is for you to break this matter to Father.'

'What? Is it love?'

'No, no, it's nothing like that. I simply like her. Besides, she's considered almost a liability by your family.'

'Then what's my position?'*

He stayed silent.

'Why don't you say something?'

'Look, Vimala, you are educated and you are now an assistant commissioner. You have nothing to worry about. We will all be happy if you find a husband. But Ranji insists that nothing is possible until you get married.'

'Oh, so you'll wait until I get married? You know, I'm going to have a brother very soon. He'll earn and find a dowry for me. After that I can get married. Would you all like to wait until

---

* it is traditional for sisters to be given in marriage in order of seniority

then? Maybe it is not beyond Ranji to do that.'

'Ay, what, is aunty pregnant? At her age? Don't talk rubbish.'

'It's true. You're going to get a tiny cousin soon. You will need a best man, won't you?' She laughed a mirthless laugh.

They walked in silence until they reached a hut. An old man was seated outside in the mild sunlight smoking a cigar. Shanmugam went up to him.

'Isn't this Velauthan's house? Is he in?'

'Daughter, someone's looking for Velauthan. Come here a minute.'

An oldish, somewhat frail figure emerged from the hut. It must have been Velauthan's mother. She was followed by a young girl, fifteen, maybe sixteen, years of age. She looked like the Mother Goddess, like a beautifully chiselled statue.

'Oh, how beautiful they are when they are young,' Vimala thought, full of admiration.

'Is Velauthan around?'

'No, he is at Velanai. For two weeks, he has not even come to see this poor girl.'

'This one?'

'Yes, his wife. My brother's daughter.'

The girl's eyes grew moist, and she seemed to tremble as she asked, 'Is he not there?'

'It is not that, Sister. We came here on some other business. We came looking for him because we thought he might escort us,' Vimala answered.

'Can we help in any way?' asked Velauthan's mother, but they walked on towards Kilinochchi town.

Siva was at the station. She didn't expect this.

'I might return tomorrow. In any case, come and check.' Did those careless parting words have so much effect?

As she alighted from the train he asked, 'What was the telegram all about?'

'Oh, that. Mother's going to give birth to a boy-child. That's why Father sent a telegram.'

'What? How can you be sure that it will be a boy?'

'Surely, isn't a boy needed to find dowries for eight girls?'

'Oh, I see. I suppose you're right.' He laughed. She too joined in. She felt her heart lighten. They emerged from the station and got into a taxi. 'Bambalapitiya. . . Pepin Lane. . . ,' he said to the driver. It was very unusual, the way he too got into the rear seat and sat close to her.

'Have you been drinking? I get the smell.'

'No. . . .' He laughed uncomfortably.

'Vimala, there's something I want to talk about. I felt I couldn't do it without a drink.'

'Don't be silly.'

'Oh, I forgot, there were two private letters for you.'

He pulled out two letters and handed them to her. One was from a friend. The other was from Chithra. She tore open the envelope and read the letter in the dim glow of the car light. 'Sister, I am doing this boldly. You know him. He is Kunam—Saravanai master's son. He works in the sugar corporation. Velauthan escorted me to his place. Without his help I couldn't have escaped from that hell. In a few days we hope to have a civil marriage. Try to come if you can. I'll let you know. I don't want anybody's blessings. But I want you to bless me, Sister.'

A short letter but clear enough. So it was Kunam. . . . Father and Mother still will not like it because he is of low caste. What nonsense. Who is bothered about caste anyway? It is all the same. He has a job. Is that not sufficient? I knew him as a boy. I wonder what he is like now? Where did Chithra find him? I remember, they were classmates. So it was from that time. . . Chithra certainly has guts.

She sighed with relief.

'What is it, Vimala?'

She didn't reply.

'Vimala, shall I buy a dinner packet for you?'

'No. Buy a broiler instead. You stay for dinner.'

'Fine, just as you please.'

He stopped the taxi close to Sharaz, went in and returned with a broiler and two bottles.

'What's in the bottles?'

'Stout.'

'So you're a stout drinker? For a moment I was scared.'

'I prefer this. But even this I take only occasionally.'

The taxi turned into Pepin Lane and came to a stop near the third house on the left. It was an upstairs house, and Vimala had the entire upstairs for herself. The hall was tastefully furnished. There were two rooms, a kitchen, and an attached bathroom.

'Siva, sit down and relax. I'll have a quick bath and then cook something for you.'

'Is the cooking to be only for today?'

She looked at him with inquiring eyes.

'Vimala dear. . . I. . . I want you.'

As he struggled for words, he moved closer to her.

'Siva, don't be sentimental. Did you drink today to tell me this?'

'Yes.'

She looked directly at the figure that was moving towards her with so much desire. Her eyes grew moist.

'Vimala, now don't you be sentimental!'

She abandoned herself completely as she embraced him and kissed him repeatedly on eyes, cheeks and lips.

'Please, Siva, stay with me tonight.'

'No, no, shouldn't we wait?'

'So. . . . .'

Both of them burst out laughing. It was a laugh that expressed the fullness of happiness and the complete release of tension.

—*Translated by C. Kanaganayakam*

Nandhi

The Spittle

Mr Panchadcharam, a schoolteacher, popularly known as 'Master' in the village, woke up one morning with a severe sore throat. He gargled with some salt water and swallowed an aspirin.

It was the day of the festival Vijayn Thasamy; he could not obtain leave from school. He had also agreed to address the school assembly that day on 'The Divine Art Set'—altogether a novel topic! Moreover, a few parents who held him in some esteem had insisted that he initiate their progeny into the alphabet on this auspicious day. Well, he had no choice! He managed to wash himself in some warm water, took another aspirin with some warm milk-coffee, and set out for school dressed in long pants and a bush shirt.

He felt feverish and stuffy; this annoyed him. He experienced a loathsome sensation as if some creature was scratching the sides of his throat from deep within.

He made his way along the village path he had come to know so well during the last eight or nine months. Many who met him in the lane nodded their heads as to an acquaintance; others stood aside respectfully and allowed him to pass. He inclined his head in reciprocation. When he came to the Kali Temple, he bowed his head and said a silent prayer. Saliva and phlegm collected in his throat. He felt he had to eject it. The need was so strong that at a bend in the lane, he cleared his throat, turned his head to the left, and expelled the saliva and phlegm. Just then, as if by previous arrangement, Annamuthu came from behind and passed him. 'She must have been to the fields adjoining the Pillaiyar Tample for her morning ablutions,' he mused.

Master thought deep and hard. Vanni and Narada with their

two *veenas**, Nandhi with his *mirudanga**, Lord Nadarajah with his *uddukku**, and Lord Krishna with his flute—what a beautiful orchestra that would be! Yes, his speech, too, would be novel. Meanwhile, Annamuthu, furious, was asking herself, 'Who is he to spit at me, this newcomer?' Her throat irritated her. 'It's all the fault of his mother-in-law and his wife,' she fumed.

When Annamuthu reached home she happened to glance over her fence and saw Kunnukku, Master's mother-in-law, collecting and heaping cow dung. She cleared her throat deliberately and spat out phlegm together with an obscenity. Kunnukku turned from her task, but did not give any sign that she had either heard Annamuthu's spitting or her obscenity. Annamuthu was disappointed. 'Whores, they've lost their heads since the coming of that Vellala groom from the town.' She muttered these words as if to herself and disappeared into her kitchen. She knew well how her words would work!

'Who did you say have lost their heads, you raving mad woman? Who did you call a whore? You're jealous because we've married off our daughter. What an evil heart you have. Well, you'll have to auction your daughter at the Pachchaivelly Fair. . . ,' retorted Kunnukku angrily.

Pathivinayagam, Annamuthu's husband, was at the well. He had just finished his bath and prayers and was still in his wet loincloth when he joined issue.

'Who are you talking to? So, we are to sell our daughter in the market? What do you say to your daughter chasing after a husband all over town? Shameless creature!' he said hotly. His daughter, coming out of the kitchen, called out to him. She had coffee in her hand. He went in. Kunnukku, too, disappeared into the kitchen.

Kunnukku was Pathivinayagam's sister. Till Master Panchadcharam had come into her household as a son-in-law, there had been no ill feeling between the two familes. In the frequent village quarrels they had stood together.

A short while later, Kunnukku's husband, Velum Mylum, emerged from the house. Standing near the cow shed, he addressed the fence: 'Men shouldn't interfere in women's quarrels. Why don't you let us live in peace?'

Annamuthu was chasing chickens in her compound. On seeing

---

* all musical instruments used in South India and Jaffna

her, Velum Mylum lost control and demanded hotly, 'Who did you call a man-chaser?'

'Why ask me? Ask your daughter,' replied Annamuthu.

'I'll break your teeth you. . . ,' warned Velum Mylum. 'Say that again and you'll see,' he challenged her.

Just then an old couple known to him came to consult him on an astrological matter. They stood hesitantly at the gate. On seeing them, Velum Mylum invited them in. 'These people, they give us no peace! Forever they look for a fight. Did you hear what they said?' he queried. The visitors had only heard what he had said. They looked at him helplessly, like lizards that had fallen into a pot of porridge.

'Come in,' he invited them again and made them sit on the *thinnai**. He then told them his story to regain his own peace of mind.

'Look here, my son-in-law's relations came to consult me regarding a marriage proposal, just like you are doing now. The horoscopes did not match. There were no adverse planets in the girl's chart, but in the boy's chart Mars was in the Seventh House! Believe me, I did not at that time think of my daughter. You see, we belong to different groups. They left the boy's chart with me. It was only then I happened to compare it with my daughter's. It matched.'

Kunnukku joined them and said, 'The neighbours—they know all this. You see, my daughter used to go to town for tutoring. They know that too. But they like to drag her name in and insult her.'

'Listen, during the wedding it was all noise and bustle. But now we've not been on talking terms for the last six years. Today being an auspicious day, they've deliberately started a quarrel.'

When Master Panchadcharam's father had heard that the horoscopes matched to near perfection, he was determined to go through with the marriage. Even the Sivan Kovil *Kurrukkal*** had said, 'You may proceed.'

The wedding took place accordingly. Pathivinayagam came to the wedding with his wife. He even blessed the newlyweds. But he refused to take part in the wedding feast. Since then, they had not been on speaking terms.

---

* *pyol*, a raised platform in an extension of the house; ** the priest of the Sivan Kovil

'What's wrong with my son? Why did Velum Mylum give his daughter in mariage to an outsider? It's money, money!' said Pathivinayagam angrily. His son had passsed the GCE Ordinary Level examination. Surely he would get a job in due course. When he thought of his son, he could hardly control his anger. 'Why should an educated boy like him be loafing in the countryside with village thugs? He even drinks toddy.'

Master was so carried away by his own performance when he spoke at the Vanni Villa that he had even forgotten his bad throat. But once the thrill was over he felt the pain again, severely this time. He did not mind it. Wasn't he in the midst of VIPs who had graced this occasion? the Circuit Education Officer, the Assistant Government Agent, a lecturer from the Training college, his own principal—they were all there and had praised him. His joy knew no bounds. He felt he had grown wings. It was then that a boy from the Pachchaivelly Village brought him an urgent message. He was to report immediately to a certain police station to make his deposition.

His 'wings' broken, he set out to the police station in a hired car. On his way he managed to get the gist of what had happened. He learned that there had been a day-long quarrel between his people and the Pathivinayagams. Nagarjan, Pathivinayagam's son, had pulled up the centre fence and destroyed it; the daughter had pelted stones. One of the stones had actually struck his mother-in-law on the head. She had it dressed at the Pachchaivelly Dispensary. His father-in-law, the astrologer Velum Mylum, had lodged a complaint at the police station. The other party on their own had also gone to the police station in a hired car. These bits of news—like newspaper headlines—he gathered from the boy.

At the police station an officer questioned him about the relationship between the two families and recorded his testimory. Then he addressed Master: 'Look, Master, whatever their differences have been in the past, you're responsible for today's incident. Annamuthu has testified that you spat at her!'

Master was perplexed. He could not remember where, when, why, or before whom he had spat at the woman. The policeman noticed his confusion and added maliciously, 'Master, you said you just made a speech at the Vanni Villa! You seem to use speech and spittle to great effect! This case will go to the courts!'

When Master emerged on to the veranda of the police station from the room where he had made his deposition, his throat itched again. Just then he saw Annamuthu and her son, Nagarajan, sitting on a bench. Her look and the irritation in his throat together brought back to him, as on film, the incident that had caused all this. This time Master Panchadcharam swallowed the saliva and the phlegm.

—Translated by S. Ranasingham

N. S. M. Ramaiya

Among the Hills

Ranjitham walked on wearily. Her face seemed flushed in the rising heat. Sweat beaded her forehead, and a few wet strands of hair had escaped the cloth she had tied around her head. Beyond her the tea-pickers still swarmed around the place where the tea leaves were being weighed. She was not fully aware that she, too, had already been there and returned. Her thoughts were fixed on the events that had taken place the previous day.

Even now her body seemed to burn as she thought of it. For one year she had awaited this event. She had woven so many dreams in her imagination, and now the very foundation seemed shattered. This was not the first occasion that Ranji's father had said no to those who came with a marriage proposal. On those earlier occasions Ranji was not surprised. In fact, she had sighed with relief. She had felt that the God to whom she prayed had steeled her father's heart to ensure her survival. Now that same God had cheated her.

Between her and Muthiah there had been 'something' for about a year. As a result she had resolved never to risk her neck for any man but him. Yesterday it was Muthiah's people who had come asking for a bride and returned empty-handed. As she wondered what she would do next, a thought, a memory, still fresh in her mind, bloomed and spread its fragrance:

It was almost noon.

The gravelled road sprinkled over with sand made the air intolerably hot. Ranji was walking rapidly as if to seek shelter in her own shadow. She carried a tiffin carrier in each hand, and on her shoulders were slung two bags from which peeped a number of thermos flasks like baby kangaroos. If the tea picking took place on a hill far away from the lines*, then someone had to take lunch to the *kanganies***.

Today it was her turn.

In the distance Muthiah was seated in the shadow of a casuarina tree sharpening a knife on a log the size of a pestle. The knife, sharpened on granules of fine sand, gleamed like silver. The bushes were being pruned on that hill. His co-workers had finished their work. There was no one but him at the time—not even a bird around. The whole mountain had taken on the appearance of a closely shaven grey head. In Muthiah's section, some bushes still stood with their heads held high, half unfinished like a single row of seedlings in a bare field.

'Whoever did that is bone lazy,' thought Ranji to herself.

Muthiah heard the approaching steps and glanced up. She was a bit surprised to see that it was indeed Muthiah's section. She knew that he was considered a 'specialist' in pruning.

He wiped the beads of sweat on his forehead with his forefinger. A thin stream of sweat rolled down. He flicked it off with his thumb a couple of times and said, 'Look, you. . . .'

Ranji was aghast. He was her brother Kandan's friend all right. In fact, he had come home on a few occasions to meet Kandan. Yet. . . she passed him, took a few steps, then paused, half turned, and asked, 'What?' The anxiety that lurked in her eyes, like that of a bewildered cat, made him laugh.

'Can you give me a little tea if you have some in there?'

The gentleness of his tone must have reassured her.

'Really?' she asked with mock scorn. 'As if you've been working so hard! Not even half the job has been completed.' Even as she said this she burst out laughing.

'What did you say? Not even half. . . ?'

Neither of them bothered to complete the sentence. Ranji started to walk.

'Do you know whose portion of work that is?' asked Muthiah, the tone of his voice a shade higher. 'Your brother's. . . it's his.'

Ranji slowed down, stopped, and then turned around to look at him. His head was bent, and he seemed to be testing the sharpness of the knife.

'This is what happens when you try to do good in this world,' he

---

* linear building consisting of attached single rooms in which tea-pickers usually live on the plantations; ** supervisors of the pickers

muttered and started whetting his knife.

She felt ashamed. Here was a man asking for a little water to quench his thirst, and she had attacked him like an enraged buffalo. She bit her lips in embarrassment, lowered the tiffin carrier and then pulled out a flask—her own blue flask. Her whole body seemed to tingle as she gently asked, 'Do you want some?'

Muthiah lifted his head. For a second there was no one to be seen. He let his eyes roam and then stopped. There was just one eye looking at him from behind a tree. Muthiah smiled mischievously. The single eye too disappeared behind the tree. He placed his palms on his knees and stood up. As he moved towards her she came out from behind the tree, placed the flask a few feet away and then retreated. He lifted the flask, opened the lid, and drank at a gulp. In a moment he wrinkled his face.

'Ah, there's no sugar!'

Ranji bit her lip to suppress her laugh and then took out a small packet of sugar from her waist. As she opened the packet and took a pinch of sugar he wiped his hand on his waist-cloth and stretched it out. A tiny mound of sugar appeared on his palm. He looked at it and said, 'Is this how you drink it? We add sugar to the tea.'

She tried to look severe. 'You are big people. You can do it that way. Can all of us afford to do the same?' Before she could finish, she turned her eyes away bashfully. Her toe was scraping the sand, causing a tiny depression.

He licked the sugar, crunched it between his teeth and drank some more tea. A few drops that fell on his chin took a winding path down to his Adam's apple.

As he returned the half-finished flask, she said, 'Give that to my brother.' She then adjusted the flasks and picked up the tiffin carriers.

'Wait just a minute,' he said.

Muthiah went back to the spot where he had been seated. He chose the low-hanging branch of the *murunga* tree, hung the flask, then sat down under a tea bush and spread out his head-cloth. Directly under the bush in the shade lay heaped almost three pounds of leaves. These he made into a bundle and gave to Ranji. As he put the bundle down in front of her and opened it, her face, eyes, and lips widened in joy and amazement.

'So much!' she said to herself.

'Take it,' he said. 'I didn't feel like pruning with the leaves still on, so I kept on picking. I suppose if I wanted to, I could have collected a lot more. Will you take it with the cloth?'

'No.'

Her waist-bag lay folded above her knees. She dropped all the leaves into the bag. A few glances at him expressed all her gratitude.

The relationship which had begun like this was now in the balance.

As Ranji walked, at a distance, Muthiah's sister Valli lowered her basket to the ground and waited for her to come up. After yesterday's incident this was going to be their first encounter, and Valli had heaps of things to talk about. She had not been unaware of the 'affair.' Yesterday's incident had shocked her.

As Ranji came up to Valli, she looked up for a moment, then lowered her eyes and continued to walk. Valli, too, kept pace with her. For some time there was a pregnant silence. Valli felt her head would burst if she didn't talk, so she touched Ranji's hand and asked, 'What happened?'

Ranji laughed a lifeless laugh. They chose a shady spot and sat down. Valli opened a flask, wiped the cup with the end of her saree, poured some tea and held it out to her. Ranji took it.

'Why did your father say that?' Valli asked. Ranji gazed at the cup and remained silent. 'You are already twenty-five. Is it not enough? How much longer are you going to wait?'

Ranji's eyes grew wet and a flood of tears rolled down her cheeks. She wiped her eyes with the cloth on her head.

'Your father is crazy about money,' said Valli with finality. 'If he lets you get married then he will lose your salary of eighty or ninety rupees, won't he?' For a few moments the surge of emotion prevented further words. 'My brother is awfully cut up,' said Valli.

'Did he say anything?' Ranji's voice trembled.

'No, nothing.' Valli, who had been gazing absently at a tea bush now turned and said gently, 'He didn't even eat last night.' Her voice shook, and Ranji breathed a deep sigh. 'Ill tell you something; will you listen?'

Ranji looked up.

'Why don't you simply come home with me?'

Ranji's eyes narrowed.

'Why not? There's no point trusting your father. Even after five years you will still be like this. You come home, and we will look after you like gold.'

Ranji felt there was some truth in what Valli said. She looked sharply at Valli for a moment and then lowered her eyes. A thousand thoughts, like the broken fragments of a sod, came crowding into her head. Should she go? What was wrong in doing that? In any case, was there an alternative? The face of Muthiah, disappointed, unable to eat, floated into her mind. A blind desire to go with Valli took possession of her.

Valli placed a hand on Ranji's shoulder and said, 'Why do you delay? Are you waiting for an auspicious hour?'

She finally came to a decision. . . to go. She did not know whether it was morally right. She did not know whether it was legally right. Yet she felt she had to do it. She had fought a tremendous battle within herself, and now she longed for comfort. If she was to continue the drudgery of her past life, she might as well soak herself in kerosene and set fire to herself. After all, even her passion was burning her.

That evening, as she held Valli's hand and stepped into their house, it was like going to the bridal bed to meet her husband. Her heart beat fast. She had been in this house a number of times. But now it was different. They hung their baskets on a nail on the wall of the veranda and stepped into the house.

It was somewhat dark inside this old line house. The house consisted of a veranda with a seat outside and one room. There was only one entrance. There was just one window in the room with bars across, almost like a jail.

Valli's mother was totally engrossed in the cooking. She had draped on a saree without a blouse revealing half her back and half her stomach. She sensed someone had come and turned. For a moment she was amazed to see Ranji. But as Valli went up to her, knelt down and explained, her face lit up, and she smiled. She came up to Ranji stroked her cheeks and pressed her fingers on the dot of paste on her forehead.

Valli snapped her knuckles. She was thoroughly elated. She dragged Ranji around to the garden and the water pipe. By the time they had a wash and returned, Valli's mother was ready with the tea. Even as Ranji drank she was reminded that at this time her tea at home would be going cold and collecting dust in the white jug. A small child—one of Valli's brothers—appeared. He was naked and stood staring at Ranji with two fingers in his mouth. Ranji drew him to her, held him close, combed back his hair, and said, 'It's not nice to run around like that. Be a good child. Go put some clothes on and come, will you?' The boy bolted, and all three of them laughed.

Ranji remembered that she too had a brother like this one. She had fed him. He insisted on sleeping by her side. Her heart melted as she thought of him. 'For how long can a girl stay in her parental home?' she thought to herself.

It was now over half an hour since she had come. Muthiah had not yet returned home. She wondered how he would react on seeing her. What she imagined was certainly soothing. However, one part of her heart had grown dark and from within the gloom came four or five crying voices. The memory of her brothers and sisters, who were her responsibility, obsessed her. Her family was large. On the earnings of three, nine members had to survive. It had been a struggle in the past. How would it be for them now?

Her mother was totally incapable of looking after the children. If their mischief became intolerable, she would merely slap her head a couple of times and scream, 'Don't kill me, you devils!' and start weeping. Weakened by repeated confinements, she, too, was like a child to Ranji. As she thought of her now, the idea of shifting her burden on to another brought a pang of guilt to her conscience. Her mother, who would enroll for work only on those rare days when she felt well, would now be compelled to work everyday. It was difficult and painful to think of her dark, emaciated mother going daily to work.

Outside the twilight dimmed, and darkness set in. Leaving Ranji alone, Valli went in and brought two lanterns, polished the chimneys, then poured some kerosene and lit them. Valli's mother had finished her cooking and gone to visit her neighbour. For a long time Ranji sat still and then quietly stood up and came close to Valli. Her eyes were moist, and her lips trembled. She said gently, 'Valli.' Even that word seemed like a sob. She wiped her nose with the edge of her saree.

As Valli looked up, it was obvious to her that Ranji had been crying for some time.

'What is it?' she asked.

'I'm going home.'

'What?'

Ranji wiped her face and nose once more. Valli stood up, shook Ranji's shoulders, and asked, 'What has come over you?'

Ranji calmly went to the clothes-line, pulled off her cloth and sack, and returned to the veranda. Valli, who had been following her, held her hand and said, 'Ranji, where are you going? Come inside.'

Ranji's eyes were now red with crying. 'No, Valli, let me to go home.' She slipped out of Valli's hold. 'It's not right, my coming like this. Do you think the earnings of my father and brother are enough for my family?' Even as she said this she felt the tears welling up within her. 'I can't bear to leave the little ones alone.' She broke down and sobbed. Valli hardly knew what to say.

The basket was taken off the nail. She put the cloth sack into it, placed the rope over her head and stepped out. She did not speak to, or even look at, Valli, who stood immobile, too stunned even to call her mother.

Ranji merged with the darkness and began to run.

—Translated by C. Kanaganayakam

Mahakavi

The Chariot and the Moon

'Let's join the crowd
That hauls the rope
To move the chariot,'
one said as he approached.

Born of Mother Earth
after hard labour
meant to live a hundred years
He came with sparkling eyes
and sinewy arms
to seek the grace of God.

He came,
a youth of lowly caste
a human being
kin to those
who spread their wings
to touch the moon
and return unscathed.

He came, bowed low
then touched the rope to haul.
'Stop,' said one,
'Hands off!' barked another,
'Spare him not!' cried a fourth.

A stone fell
A head split.
Teeth broken

faces disfigured
blood spilt
the earth reddened
and in the commotion
humans were massacred.

Abruptly
the moving chariot
stopped.
The mother who bore the Earth
sat mute
watched in horror
this frenzied passion.

Behold, the kin of men
who spread his wings
to touch the moon,
writhing in pain
on the bloody dust.

—Translated by S. Pathmanathan

Mahakavi

A Wish

Although the sky is heavy with dark clouds
Yet the due season never brings the rain
Even the cactus-thorns sobbed on the plant
You work, and this state wakes my wonder.

The ox does not draw and the plough does not move
In rainless lands the dry sand proves a snare
Pouring your sweat to quench the fires that glow
This earth's made festive since you make grain grow.

For water with your hands you scoop the soil
To protect the plants squeeze blood and flesh
One blade, then two, the green sheath, pregnant swells
Who is it but you who understands earth's ways so well?

Against his lips the budding stalks he lifts
To kiss 'see—these gold pieces—Gods own gift!'
Paddy buds are dancing twirling gold dust of the earth
A living death—yet all he asks is this.

When the lips of field bunds are parched with heat
Then comes the month where there is naught to eat
As the grain matures rain winds brawl anew
O God, of power, Aiyyanaar, where are you?

—Translated by Mendis Rohanadeera

R. Murugaiyan

Toil

The festival chariot shines
In its majestic grandeur
Reaching out high
Into the blue sky.

The bulls below, yoked to the chariot
Are thoroughly exhausted,
Panting, foaming at their mouths.
The chariot moves because the bulls pull.

But the decorative wooden horses
On the prominent top row.
Remain in their proud galloping poses.
Most of the people have lost sight of
The exhausted old beasts below.

—*Translated by the author*

Sillaiyoor Selvarajan

I Shall Be God

I shall be God, I shall be God,
I shall be God—Be the Lord of the Word!

Humans of the earth shall all adore me
in their hearts and minds with reverent glee!
Till eternity ends my Word shall permeate,
in Tamil so chaste, I shall magic CREATE!

I shall be God—the Lord of CREATION!

All that I deem as truths shall prevail!
My lofty philosophies, the World shall hail!
A Word from me shall PROTECT them all!
Death shall never, over them befall!

I shall be God—the Lord of PROTECTION!

Whoever dares to trample the lives
of good men of deeds, on them my Word drives
the laser fire beam of my fuming Third Eye!
My satiric writ shall DESTROY—they die!

I shall be God—the Lord of DESTRUCTION!

If it be fact that the Word was made Flesh,
it shall be done once more afresh!
With the trinitive Power wrested from the Lord,
I shall be Almighty God of the Word!

—Translated by the author

Sillaiyoor Selvarajan

I Submit My Heart to the Salt-Giver!

Hark, deep sea!
O! Benevolent Mother!
Chronicles of yore
proudly declare,
five rare precious treasures,
to man you spare!
I care not for your conches,
I care not for those shells,
Your rich coral stones
and your valueless pearls, I scorn!
But I submit my humble heart
and venerate you Great Goddess,
for the pinch of salt you grant
for the sparse gruel of the
poorest man!

—*Translated by the author*

Kurunji Nathan

Where is Justice? Here We Go. . . .

Tilling hill and dale we worked laboriously
We bore anguish with no rest to body and soul
Turned out of our homeland we leave these shores;
Sir. . . .
We go helpless, destitute

Full many a crore's worth in gold we produced
Worry and suffering was all our lot
How little we saved, and of that too we are dispossessed;
Sir to the South country we go
Helpess, destitute

'Stateless' were we branded and stigmatized
As outcast vagabonds at the bottom we remain
With shattered and bleeding hearts we leave
O Sir
Like dumb cattle benumbed we go.

With honour we lived our lives, scarcity riddled;
Heart and soul battered and crushed by labour
Maimed and disabled we set forth
Where, Sir, where is justice. . . .
Banished from our home and land we go.
Parents and children and our generations we leave
Them we leave ready fodder to the gulping earth
Our feet drag and tears flow as we leave
Oh, Sir. . . .
Huddled in a ship to an unseen land we go.

—Translated by Mendis Rohanadeera

M.A. Nuhman

Our Grandpa Had
an Elephant

In my childhood I remember,
Our good Grandpa
Owned a handsome tusker
I remember it yet;

The might of his tusker
Was known throughout the world:
If you do not know it
It is worth knowing today—

Grandfather had gone round the world astride this majestic
    tusker
Gone beyond the Atlantic and rounded China
Had sojourned in far off Andalusian plains
For eight long centuries our Grandpa had mounted this
    elephant;

We descend from ancestors who reigned mounted on
    elephants
We ruled half the world and admonished the whole world
Slipped from our hand, arts and sciences enlightened land by
    land
Thus our Grandpa's splendid tusker was renowned in the
    world

White men who came to Baghdad to gain knowledge
Will repeat this
And it has been written

Along the world famed plains of Andalusia!

Once upon a time our Grandfather had a mighty tusker
The whole world knew its might; if you did not, know it now,
    friend
Did your Grandpa own an elephant?
And was it a tusker?

Where is that elephant now
Tell me, grandson
Where is your tusker?
Answer that now—

You do not seem
Certainly do not seem
To be a grandson of an elephant owner

You have come here with aching feet
Crumpled rags and pinched face

Did your Grandpa own an elephant
A tusker elephant—pray, tell!

Where is that elephant now
Tell O grandson
Where is your tusker?
Answer that now

Where is our tusker
Where did the tusker go?

'We who shed blood
To build the heavenly Kingdom
On behalf of God the Creator
We abandoned that sole path;
Since we abandoned it
And the prayers offered in sorrow
Falling on our knees
Because we abandoned
Spiritual power, primal truth—

We have lost our mighty tusker
We know, and feel it now

'Our noble Gandpa owned
A splendid tusker.'
Why do the younger generation
With oppressed lips
Sing the same old song?
What was borrowed
From the poet Iqbal*
Why must they sing it again?

Grandson,
Think for a moment inwardly
Grandson of an elephant owner
Think inwardly, deeply

Whether the odour of blood
Is there on the sword blade of the Umayyads

Whether the taste of blood
Is there in the corners of the palace of the Abbasids
Whether the colour of blood
Is smeared on the headgear of Sultans,
Do think a moment
O grandson

Did you recognize the odour of blood
To whom does that odour belong
Diffused and spread like the Red Sea
Whose is that blood?

Alas! is the blood
That of your Grandsire?
Yes, your Grandsires
To capture power
Wrestling with each other

---

* reference to Iqbal's famous poem 'Shikwah Jawab-e Shikwah' ('The Answer to the Complaint'). Nuhman's poem is, in a sense, a reply to Iqbal.

Shed their blood and
That wafting odour is of it.

Every time they fought
In lust of power
They died crushed by elephants

To see those enthroned on elephants
Was the only luck
Of you who followed the elephants, trailing behind them.

While they sat on thrones
Adorned with inlaid rubies
You all were
Seated on the worn-out mat counting elephants in the
    procession!

In their mansion
You all with aching hands
Weaving glittering velvet curtains
Waited on the worn-out mat!

In palaces on luxurious beds
Embracing and sporting with playful damsels
Are they, whose soft carpets weaving
You sat on the worn-out mat for too long a time!

They in their harems
Marble terrace of Taj Mahal
Built in the name of Wine, Song and Dance
Polished with our drops of sweat.

Those grandfathers
Drank and ate in golden vessels
While on your fireless hearth
Cats were sleeping!
—So grandson
Do you see the relationship
The tie binding you and your Grandsires
Do you see what it is
Today, at least?

The Grandsires were of royal line
We, the grandchildren are of the working class
You have not been deprived of anything
Do you have anything to be dispossessed of?

It was those of royal pedigree who owned and lost the
    elephant
It was they who had palaces and they who lost them
Grandson, a great fire flared up in Europe's Centre
It was the scions of Royalty who tumbled and perished in
    that blaze

By the whirlwinds their palaces were flung to the sky
Caught by that fire their gemmed thrones were razed to the
    ground
Your Grandsires fell from their thrones and white men
    reigned then
Shorn of his might, the great elephant dwindled day by day

Grandson
Nothing have you lost
Have you anything
To lose?

How do you regain
That which you have lost once?
Your Grandsires and their scholars
Their writers, poets
Were resurrected and came.

The grandson who stood aside
Having naught to lose
They caught by the neck
And called to him loudly
'. . . Child, child, arise!
Your valued treasures
Are grabbed from you! awake!
Arise! awake! march onward!
Of old you were heroes who ruled the earth!
With hosts mounted on elephants you were great heroes!
Royal princes who freed the world!

What has happened today, O children?
Must we still wait with empty hands?
The time has come
Awake! arise! march onward!'

It is time to awaken
Your Grandsires and their scholars
Their writers, their poets
Arose and came and aroused you.

Your Grandsires were the rulers
We the grandsons are of the working class

Once enfeebled
The mighty elephant
Revitalized
Awakened again
Arose.

The flames arose in Africa and Asia
Nationalism burst into great rebellions
Once more the strong odour of blood spread everywhere
The white men have fallen and your Grandsires are
    enthroned.

Then grandson
True is this word
Once again they are on the throne.

To watch them approach
Enthroned on high
As you sit on your mats
Is the boon you have gained!

So grandson
That is all that has happened
Do you all know that fact even now?
You have never lost anything—
Nor did you ever own
Anything to lose.

Though banners with crescents wave
Do you recall what happened yesterday
Under the shelter of those banners?

Grandson of your Grandsires
Think for a moment
Think inwardly, deeply

The blood spilled
Among the clods
Of Indonesia's soil
Scent out.

The blood that flowed
On Jordan's soil
By the banks of the river
Scent out.

The blood clotting the mud
On the river-banks
Of Bangladesh
Scent out.

Who shed
This clotted blood
Scent out.

Whose bullets
Pierced the breasts
Of those whose blood was shed
Scent out.

Is there not one God only
For you and for them?
Is it not the same *Koran*
That both worship and read?
Until false words keep you
Seemingly equal
You can live together at the feet of God!

Grandson of your Grandsires,
Open your eyes
Arise!

They are not your kin
But beasts that devoured you.

Decking every corner of the sky
With strings of flags glowing with crescents
Creating illusions of brotherhood
They were only beasts of prey who exploited you.

    —All who live with mansions
    Soft beds
    Regal power
    Great pride
    Are on one side.

    —All who live with hunger
    Thirst
    Lamentation
    And the fire of sorrow
    Are on one side.

—Grandson of your Grandsires,
Awake, arise,
Stand on the ashes
Of false brotherhood
And recognize
Your own comrades aright.

    —Translated by Mendis Rohanadheera

M.A.Nuhman

Murder

Last night
I had a dream
Lord Buddha was shot dead
by the police—
guardians of the law.
His body lay drenched in blood
on the step
of the Jaffna Library*!

Under cover of darkness
came the ministers.
'His name—not in our lists!
Why did you kill him?'
they ask in anger.

'No, sirs, no!
There was no mistake.
Without bumping him off
it was impossible
to harm even a fly.
Therefore. . .', they stammered.

'Okay, okay!
Hide the corpse.'
The ministers vanish.

---

* Jaffna Public Library was burned down in an incident of ethnic violence

The men in civvies
dragged the corpse
into the library.
They heaped the books,
rare and valuable,
ninety thousand in all.
They lit the pyre
with the *Cikalokavada Sutta**.
Thus the remains
Of the Compassionate One
were burned to ashes
along with the *Dhammapada***.

—*Translated by S. Pathmanathan*

---

* titles of Buddhist texts; **collection of the teachings of the Buddha

Notes on the Authors

Writers in English

ARASANAYAGAM, JEAN: Lecturer in English, Teachers' College, Peradeniya, Sri Lanka; published volumes of poetry include *Kindura* (1973), *Apocalypse '83* (1984), *A Colonial Inheritance and Other Poems* (1985) and *Out of our Prisons we Emerge* (1987).

CHRYSOSTOM, REGGIE: Emigrated to England, but continues to contribute poetry regularly to reputed Sri Lankan journals.

DE ALWIS, RENTON: Formerly Director of Sri Lanka's Tourist Board, he now works for the island's Open University and writes poetry occasionally.

FERNANDO, CHITRA: Senior Lecturer in Linguistics at Macquarie University, Australia; author of several collections of stories for children and two collections for adults, *Three Women* (1983) and *Between Worlds* (1988).

FERNANDO, PATRICK: Staff officer in Sri Lanka's Department of Inland Revenue until his premature death; first volume of poems, *The Return of Ulysses* (1955); *Selected Poems* (1984) appeared posthumously.

GOONERATNE, YASMINE: Associate Professor in English at Macquarie University, Australia; critic and editor; published three volumes of poetry, *Word Bird Motif* (1971), *The Lizard's Cry and Other Poems* (1972) and *6000 ft Death Dive* (1981).

GOONEWARDENE, JAMES: Formerly a broadcaster with long experience in the medium; author of the novels *A Quiet Place* (1961), *Call of the Kirala* (1971), *An Asian Gambit* (1985), *Dream Time River* (1985), *One Mad Bid for Freedom* (1990), and a collection of stories, *The Awakening of Doctor Kirthi* (1976).

GUNATILLAKE, GODFREY: Critic and creative writer soon after graduating; joined the Ceylon Civil Service in which he held several important positions; now Director of the Marga Institute for Development Studies.

KARUNARATNE, SUVIMALEE: Formerly a journalist and freelance broadcaster; author of *Bili Pooja*—Human Sacrifice (1973), a collection of stories; contributes fiction regularly to reputed local journals.

OBEYESEKERE, RANJINI: Critic and translator; formerly of the Department of English at the University of Peradeniya and later at the University of California, San Diego; presently engaged in translating Sinhalese literary works.

RANASINGHE, ANNE: Published volumes of poetry include *Poems* (1971), *With Words We Write Our Lives, Past, Present and Future* (1972), *Plead Mercy* (1976) and *Against Eternity and Darkness* (1985).

SCHAREN, PETER: Emigrated to Australia, where he has worked in the Taxation Department in Sydney; published collections of poetry include *Twenty-Four A.M.* (1972), *Southern Village and September 1973* (1973), *Signs and Seas* (1980) and *Rain Blows* (1981).

SIRIWARDENA, REGGIE: Critic, translator, playwright and civil rights activist; presently editor, International Centre for Ethnic Studies, Colombo; published original poetry in *Waiting for the Soldier* (1989) and *To the Muse of Insomnia* (1990).

TISSAINAYAGAM, J.S. : Journalist; contributed several stories to local journals.

WIJENAIKE, PUNYAKANTE: author of *The Third Woman* (1963) and *The Rebel* (1979), both collections of stories, the novel *The Waiting Earth* (1966), the novella *Giraya* (1971), and most recently, a kind of memoir, *A Way of life* (1987).

WIKKRAMASINHA, LAKDASA: Instructor in English at the University of Kelaniya until his premature death; published collections of poetry include *Nossa Senhora dos Chingalas* (1973), *O Regal Blood* (1975) and *Grasshopper Gleaming* (1976).

Writers in Sinhalese

AMERASEKERA, GUNADASA: Dentist by profession, he has always found time for literary pursuits; critic, poet and novelist; early work shows the influence of Western writers and forms but he now looks more to native sources for inspiration.

DISSANAYAKE, WIMAL: Currently Assistant Director, Institute of Culture and Communication, East-West Center, Honolulu, Hawaii; numerous publications include several collections of poetry in Sinhalese, such as *Akal Vassa* (Unseasonal Rains), *Rav Pilirav* (Sounds and Echoes), and critical works on Sinhalese literature.

GUNASINGHE, SIRI: Scholar, univerity teacher, art historian, novelist, poet, critic and film director; most popular volumes of poetry are *Mas Le Nati Ata* (Bones Without Flesh and Blood) and *Abhinikmana* (Renunciation); now Professor of South Asian Art at the University of Victoria, Canada.

KODITUWAKKU, PARAKRAMA: Well-known as a poet and critic; published several volumes of poetry, including *Alut Minihek Avit* (A New Man Has Come); also wrote short fiction and for a while was editor of the socialist literary journal *Mawatha* (The Path).

KURUVITA BANDARA, THILAKARATNE: Published several volumes of poetry and short stories, including *Deviyo Thathi Gena Maha Polovata Ei*—The Gods Alarmed, Descend to Earth (1971).

NAVAGATTEGAMA, SIMON: Well-known as a dramatist, novelist and short-story writer; his play *Subha Saha Yasa*—The King and his Attendant (1974) enjoyed phenomenal success, while his highly popular novel, *Suddilage Kathava*—The Story of Suddi and Others, has recently been made into a film; presently works for UNICEF.

PERERA, KARUNA: Author of a novel, *Suriya Udavena Thuru*—Until the Sun Rises; best known for her short stories *Andurata Eliyak*—A Light in the Darkness and *Eko Math Eka Rataka*—Once upon a Time; also publishes in both literary journals and the features sections of daily newspapers.

RUWANPATHIRANA, MONICA: Teacher by profession; published several volumes of poetry, including a volume to mark International Woman's Year, *Obe Yeheliya Aya Gehaniya*—Your Friend She is Woman; recognized as one of the leading women poets.

SARACHCHANDRA, EDIRIWIRA: Formerly Professor of Pali and later Professor of Modern Sinhalese Literature; critic and playwright in Sinhalese; novelist in both English and Sinhalese; winner of the Asan World Prize in 1983 and the Ramon Magsaysay Award in 1988.

SEKERA, MAHAGAMA: Well-known and prolific poet; published five volumes of poetry, three novels, translations of prose works and drama, and several collections of children's stories and songs; important work, *Prabudha*—The Sage— appeared posthumously in 1977.

Writers in Tamil

MAHAKAVI (T. RUDRAMOORTHY): Major Tamil poet; published his first collection in 1955; during his most productive period, 1960 to 1970, he wrote five epics and seven verse plays.

MURUGAIYAN, R.: Biographical data not available.

NANDHI (C. SIVAGNANASUNDERAM): Professor of Community Medicine at the University of Jaffna; wrote two novels and several short stories; also publishes educational non-fiction.

NATHAN, KURUNJI: Biographical data not available.

NUHMAN, M.A.: Lecturer in the Department of Tamil and Linguistics at the University of Jaffna; editor of the Tamil quarterly *Poet*; wrote a collection of long poems which has been translated into Sinhalese.

RAMAIYA, N.S.M.: Writes short fiction about plantation workers; his first collection, *A Basketful of Tea Leaves*, appeared in 1980.

SADDANATHAN, K.: Presently associated with the Tamil daily *Veerakesari*; published his collection of short fiction, *Change*, in 1980; work features problems of women in Jaffna society.

SELVARAJAN, SILLAIYOOR (THANTHONRI-K-KAVIRAYAR): Presently a mass communications consultant; one of the foremost Tamil poets; has written over three thousand short and long poems and has published three books; also a journalist, playwright, writer of fiction, broadcaster and stage-film-television artiste.

THAMBIRAJAH,P: Presently Chief Librarian of the American Center; writes occasionally.

MORE ABOUT PENGUINS

For further information about books available from Penguins in India write to Penguin Books (India) Ltd, B4/246, Safdarjung Enclave, New Delhi 110 029.

In the UK: For a complete list of books available from Penguins in the United Kingdom write to Dept. EP, Penguin Books Ltd, Harmondsworth, Middlesex UB7 0DA.

In the U.S.A.: For a complete list of books available from Penguins in the United States write to Dept. DG, Penguin Books, 299 Murray Hill Parkway, East Rutherford, New Jersey 07073.

In Canada: For a complete list of books available from Penguins in Canada write to Penguin Books Canada Ltd, 2801 John Street, Markham, Ontario L3R 1B4.

In Australia: For a complete list of books available from Penguins in Australia write to the Marketing Department, Penguin Books Australia Ltd, P.O. Box 257, Ringwood, Victoria 3134.

In New Zealand: For a complete list of books available from Penguins in New Zealand write to the Marketing Department, Penguin Books (N.Z.) Ltd, Private Bag, Takapuna, Auckland 9.

THE MIDDLEMAN AND OTHER STORIES
Bharati Mukherjee

Passionate, comic, violent and ultimately tender these eleven award-winning stories portray new immigrants in America: a proud and proper Tamil Sri Lankan whose ten thousand mile journey falls short of its end, if not of its goal; a fumbling insecure Bengali man attempting to seduce a liberated Indian woman in Iowa; an Indian student in New York taking her husband around the city and wondering if 'freed from the dignities of old world culture, he too could get drunk and squirt...Cheez Whiz on a guest...' Taken together the collection reveals in perfect detail a new, exciting and exuberant world in our midst.

'These stories are outrageous, elegiac, unforgiving, regretful, and necessary, and they don't let anyone off the hook.... Bharati Mukherjee at her at her dire best.'

— *Margaret Atwood*

FAIR TREE OF THE VOID

Vilas Sarang
Translated from the Marathi by the author and
Breon Mitchell

In a startling blend of the real and the fantastic, these stories create a world populated wholly by solitaries—usually lonely single males who lead sterile, aimless lives. As a function of their passivity, these characters often find themselves drawn into extraordinary situations where the bizarre is commonplace: one protagonist is cast ashore on an island where there are only half women, another metamorphoses into a giant penis, a third is witness to idols of gods in a festival procession coming alive and disappearing into the streets of Bombay .... Sarang's world, then, is one that is poised between the provinces of imagination and reality—and the obvious influences are the great masters of this form of literature—Kafka, Camus, Beckett and Borges. Yet, Sarang's voice is unique in that he transcends those who have gone before to emerge in a place that we have never visited, the true hallmark of a writer of genius.

THE PENGUIN BOOK OF
MODERN INDIAN SHORT STORIES
Edited by Stephen Alter & Wimal Dissanayake

Some of the stories included in this volume—by Bharati Mukherjee, Anita Desai, Raja Rao, U.R. Anantha Murthy and Bhisham Sahni for example—have already been widely anthologized and are well-known around the world. The others will be less familiar to the reader but are nonetheless classics of the art of the short story. Taken as a whole, *The Penguin Book of Modern Indian Short Stories* is a marvellous and entertaining introduction to the rich diversity of pleasures that the Indian short story—a form that has produced masters in over a dozen languages—at its best can offer.